D1117077

Partition
of Cell Particles and
Macromolecules

PER-ÅKE ALBERTSSON

Partition
of Cell Particles and
Macromolecules

Distribution and fractionation of cells, viruses,
microsomes, proteins, nucleic acids, and antigen-antibody
complexes in aqueous polymer two-phase systems

ALMQVIST & WIKSELL
STOCKHOLM
GÖTEBORG · UPPSALA
·
JOHN WILEY & SONS
NEW YORK

PRINTED IN SWEDEN BY

Almqvist & Wiksells

BOKTRYCKERI AKTIEBOLAG

UPPSALA 1960

Foreword

At the Institute of Biochemistry in Uppsala much attention has been paid to the development of separation methods suitable for the study of biochemical systems, especially such as contain substances of large molecular weight. In work of this kind one must always keep in mind that such systems are easily destroyed in many of the common chemical operations. Consequently gentle methods—many of them based upon simple physical phenomena—have proved particularly useful when dealing with this kind of materials. Also the methods should be highly specific, as minute differences in structure or composition may be of decisive importance for the functional properties of biochemically important macromolecules. When speaking of separation, one naturally thinks of the purification and isolation of substances in the first place. It is obvious, however, that separation methods play a decisive part also in the determination of the structure of complicated large molecules, when this is attempted by a study of fragments of such molecules, separated out from complex mixtures obtained, for example, by hydrolysis.

During the last few years we have been interested in exploring the possibilities of improving methods for the separation of particles of biological origin. The reason for this is obvious. Submicroscopic particles, such as microsomes, viruses, and bacteriophages occupy a very important position in present biochemical research. Also whole cells, cell nuclei, cell fragments and membranes, and many other particulate materials are of considerable interest and there is a great need for improved, specific methods for their isolation in quantities. Again, a realisation of the importance of such work as an approach to structural problems has also been in our minds, and part of the work has been done in correlation with electron microscope investigations.

Of several approaches attempted the procedure described in this book appears to be particularly interesting and useful. The author has done this work in fulfillment of the requirements for the degree of Doctor of Philosophy at the University of Uppsala. Part of the work has been published earlier in scientific journals, but this book contains the most complete and up-to-date description of the method. Thus this work is a dissertation, but it has purposely been written in a manner which deviates somewhat from the typical doctor's thesis. Thus it gives a thorough description of the theoretical background and also extensive practical details of interest to those who would wish to apply the method to their problems. Already the first publication of the method gave rise to a great many inquiries, and evidently the method has rapidly come into general use. Therefore I advised the author to plan this book also as a sort of practical guide.

The method, in all its simplicity, seems to offer a great many possibilities, and is by no means fully explored in all its modifications yet. The work is being continued both in Uppsala and elsewhere. Such work is facilitated if other research workers try it in their problems, and thus widen the experience on which a further improvement must rest.

We are very much indebted to Messrs. Almqvist and Wiksell, Uppsala and to John Wiley and Sons, New York, for their willingness to publish and distribute this monograph.

Uppsala, November 1st, 1960

ARNE TISELIUS

Contents

Preface

The main part of the investigations described in this book has been carried out at the Institute of Biochemistry, University of Uppsala, Uppsala, Sweden. Part of the work has been previously published; see reference nos. 1–9, 14, 21, and 24 of Chapter 1.

I wish to thank Prof. A. Tiselius for his encouragement and advice, and also my collaborators Drs. G. Frick, L. Broman and T. Lif, Institute of Biochemistry, Prof. T. Wesslén and Dr. L. Philipson, Institute of Virology, Uppsala, Dr. G. Toschi, Instituto Superiore di Sanitá, Rome, Dr. V. Hanzon, Institute of Anatomy, Uppsala, Dr. Ed. J. Nyns, University of Louvain, Belgium, Dr. E. Norrby, Institute of Virology, Karolinska Institutet, Stockholm, and all members of the staff of the Institute of Biochemistry, Uppsala, for helpful discussions.

Further, I wish to thank Miss I. Andersson for skilful technical assistance, Mr. G. Forsling for drawing the figures, and Drs. N. Marsden and W. Brown for correcting the English.

This work has been supported financially by the Swedish Technical Research Council, the Swedish Natural Research Council, the Swedish Medical Research Council, and the U.S. Department of Army, through its European Office, under contract numbers DA-91-508-EUC-287, DA-91-591-EUC-1025, and DA-91-591-EUC-1462.

The following figures and tables have appeared in publications of different journals and the respective copyright owners are thanked for permission to reproduce them: Figs. 4.20, 5.2, 5.3, 5.4, 8.1 and 8.2 (Macmillan & Co., Ltd., London); part of Table 4.7 (Elsevier Publishing Company, Amsterdam); Tables 4.12 and 7.9 (Springer-Verlag, Vienna); Tables 4.14, 6.1, 7.6, 7.8 and 7.10, and Figs. 6.3, 6.4 and 6.5 (Academic Press, Inc., New York).

Uppsala, October, 1960   PER-ÅKE ALBERTSSON

1. Introduction

The isolation of subcellular particles from disrupted cells is becoming of increasing importance in biochemistry. The study of isolated mitochondria, microsomes, and chloroplasts, for example, has given much information on both the chemistry and function of these particles, and it has thus become possible to attack one of the fundamental problems in biochemistry: the relation between structure and function in the living cell.

For the isolation of certain important biochemical substances such as hormones and enzymes, which are localized in a particulate structure of the cell, particle fractionation methods can be used. It may thus be advantageous to extract the hormone or enzyme from the isolated particulate structure rather than from the whole cell.

It is probable that some of the cell particle isolation techniques which are now used in the laboratory will in the future find application also on an industrial scale. Efficient methods for the fractionation of cell particles are therefore of great importance. Hitherto, centrifugation has been the most frequently used method, chiefly because its basic principles are well understood and centrifuges fulfilling the various requirements are now commercially available. By differential centrifugation, the particles are separated mainly by difference in mass while density gradient centrifugation allows a separation according to the density of the particles. By the latter method, extremely specific fractionations may be achieved as in the separation of two deoxyribonucleic acid preparations differing in the nitrogen isotope only; one with ^{14}N and the other with ^{15}N (18).

With the highly diversified properties of cell particles it is of course an advantage to be able to use methods where differences in other properties such as surface properties and the electrical charge of the particles are utilized for separation. Methods such as chromatography and zone electrophoresis, which are based upon these properties, have also been applied to cellular particles. In this book the fractionation of macromolecules and cell particles[1] by distribution in liquid–liquid two-phase systems will be discussed. By this method particles are separated mainly by differences in their surface properties.

Separation of substances by partition is a classical and perhaps the most widespread method in organic chemistry, both in the laboratory and on an industrial scale. In inorganic chemistry liquid–liquid extraction has also found many applications, for example in the separation of nuclear fuels and as an analytical tool (19). In biochemistry, most of the partition methods used have been applied to low molecular substances. Thus, the method of countercurrent distribution (12) developed by Craig and co-workers has been used for the separation of peptides, hormones and vitamins. In recent years, a number of proteins (13, 23) have also been separated by partition methods. Herbert & Pinsent (17), in their procedure for purification of catalase, included an extraction step in a phase system of ammonium sulfate, water, and ethanol. Other similar phase systems composed of salt, water, and various glycol derivatives were constructed by Martin & Porter for use in the partition chromatography of proteins. For references, see the reviews by Porter (22) and Tavel & Signer (23). A water–phenol system was introduced by Gierer & Schramm (16) for the isolation of infective nucleic acid from viruses and this method has been widely used. The virus protein is transferred to the phenol phase, in a denatured form, while the nucleic acid remains in the aqueous phase. Another phase system, introduced by Gessler *et al.* and used in virus research, is a mixture of water and a fluorocarbon (15). In this case the virus particles remain in the aqueous phase while some impurities collect in the organic phase. Both these latter phase systems act, however, as selective denaturing agents, destroying the "impurities" and leaving the substance of interest more or less intact.

So far, partition methods have therefore mainly been applied to stable low molecular proteins and peptides but it would be of the greatest interest if liquid–liquid partition could also be applied to

---

[1] The term cell particles means whole cells and particles, including viruses, derived from the disintegration of cells; the particles thus have a size ranging from 0.01 to 10 microns. The term 'macromolecules' is used here to describe molecules in the molecular weight range between 50 000 and 10 000 000, for example proteins and nucleic acids.

very high molecular weight substances, because there is a greater chance of obtaining a state of equilibrium between two liquid phases than between a solid phase and a liquid phase, for example. This is particularly so when macromolecules are involved. Although, in precipitation or in adsorption, where proteins are distributed between a solid and a liquid phase, equilibrium is supposed to be established under ideal conditions, it is well known that this is difficult to realize. Liquid–liquid partitioning therefore would be an equilibrium method which should offer considerable potentialities for studying biological macromolocules.

Special problems arise when a phase system has to be selected for particles of biological origin. The phase system should be as "mild" as possible, meaning that consideration must be paid to the water content, ionic composition, osmotic pressure, ability to dissolve out substances from the particles, denaturing effects, etc. Due to their large size, cell particles usually distribute unilaterally in a two-phase system. Brønsted and co-workers (10, 11) demonstrated long ago, both theoretically and experimentally, that the larger the particle size of the partitioned substance the more one-sided the distribution. He deduced the following approximate formula

$$K = e^{\frac{M\lambda}{kT}}$$

where K is the partition coefficient, that is the ratio between the concentrations of the partitioned substance in the top and bottom phases, M the molecular weight, k the Boltzmann constant, and λ a constant characteristic for the substance and the phase system. Larger particles (M large) will therefore collect in either of the phases depending upon the sign of λ. When, as sometimes happens, two substances concentrate in different phases, this unilateral distribution is useful since it gives a good separation. When two substances have an affinity for the same phase, there is no separation, but if a system can be found which yields a partition coefficient between 0.1–10, multiple extractions such as in countercurrent distribution may be used to achieve separation.

Several of the problems mentioned above rule out most of the conventional phase systems containing organic solvents. Instead, a number of aqueous polymer two-phase systems have been used for the present study. These systems yield phases rich in water and allow a reproducible partition of even fragile particles and macromolecules under mild conditions (1–9, 14, 20, 21, 24). Since the success of any partition method depends much on the proper choice of solvent system, these phase systems have been studied in detail, and their properties will be described in the next chapter.

REFERENCES

1. ALBERTSSON, P. Å., *Nature, 177*, 771 (1956).
2. — *Biochim. Biophys. Acta, 27*, 378 (1958).
3. — *Nature, 182*, 709 (1958).
4. — *Biochem. Pharmacol.* (1960), in press.
5. ALBERTSSON, P. Å., and FRICK, G., *Biochim. Biophys. Acta, 37*, 230 (1960).
6. ALBERTSSON, P. Å., HANZON, V., and TOSCHI, G., *J. Ultrastructure Res., 2*, 366 (1959).
7. ALBERTSSON, P. Å., and NYNS, Ed. J., *Nature, 184*, 1465 (1959).
8. — *Arkiv Kemi* (1960), in press.
9. ALBERTSSON, P. Å., and PHILIPSON, L., *Nature, 185*, 38 (1960).
10. BRØNSTED, J. N., *Z. phys. Chem., A.* (Bodenstein-Festband), 257 (1931).
11. BRØNSTED, J. N., and WARMING, E., *Z. phys. Chem., A, 155*, 343 (1931).
12. CRAIG, L. C., and CRAIG, D., *in* Technique of Organic Chemistry, edited by A. Weissberger, Vol. III, Part 1, second edition, Intersience Publishers, Inc., New York, 1956.
13. CRAIG, L. C., *in* A Laboratory Manual of Analytical Methods of Protein Chemistry, edited by ALEXANDER, P., and BLOCK, R. J., Vol. 1, p. 121, Pergamon Press, Oxford, 1960.
14. FRICK, G., and ALBERTSSON, P. Å., *Nature, 183*, 1070 (1959).
15. GESSLER, A. E., BENDER, C. E., and PARKINSON, M. C., *Trans. N.Y. Acad. Sci., 18* (2), 701 (1956).
16. GIERER, A., and SCHRAMM, G., *Z. Naturforsch., 11b*, 138 (1956).
17. HERBERT, D., and PINSENT, J., *Biochem. J., 43*, 193 (1948).
18. MESELSON, M., and STAHL, F. W., *Proc. Natl. Acad. Sci. U.S., 44*, 671 (1958).
19. MORRISON, G. H., and FREISER, H., Solvent Extraction in Analytical Chemistry, John Wiley & Sons, Inc., New York, 1957.
20. NORRBY, E., and ALBERTSSON, P. Å., *Nature*, in press.
21. PHILIPSON, L., ALBERTSSON, P. Å., and FRICK, G., *Virology, 11*, 553 (1960).
22. PORTER, R. R., in COLOWICK, S. P., and KAPLAN, N. N., Methods in Enzymology, Vol. 1, p. 98, Academic Press, Inc. New York, 1955.
23. TAVEL, P. v., and SIGNER, R., *Advances in Protein Chem., 11*, 237 (1956).
24. WESSLÉN, T., ALBERTSSON, P. Å., and PHILIPSON, L., *Arch. Virusforsch., 9*, 510 (1959).

2. Liquid Polymer Phase Systems

INTRODUCTION

If a 2.2 per cent aqueous solution of dextran is mixed in a test tube with an equal amount of a 0.72 per cent aqueous solution of methyl-cellulose, the mixture becomes turbid, and if the tube is allowed to stand for a while two liquid, viscous layers are formed. Analysis of these will show that the bottom layer contains most of the dextran and the top layer most of the methylcellulose, as may be seen in Fig. 2.1. If the mixture is further shaken and allowed to stand, the two layers will again separate out. There is thus a system containing two immiscible phases in equilibrium, both phases being rich in water. The difference in the properties of the two phases is small compared with ordinary two-phase systems such as water–ether and water–benzene. The difference between the densities and the refractive indices of the two phases is also very small. The small refractive index difference sometimes even makes it difficult to detect the interface. The phase boundary has a very small interfacial tension and forms almost a right angle with the wall of the test tube.

Such liquid phase separation in mixtures containing one or more colloids was first reported in the literature long ago. Beijerinck in 1896 observed that if aqueous solutions of gelatin and agar, or gelatin and soluble starch (but not agar and soluble starch) were mixed, a turbid mixture which separated into two liquid layers was obtained (4, 5). The bottom layer contained most of the agar (or starch) and the top layer most of the gelatin. These systems were later studied in detail by Ostwald & Hertel (38, 39) who found that, for starches from different sources, different concentrations were necessary for phase separation.

In a systematic investigation Dobry & Boyer-Kawenoki (13) studied the miscibility of a large number of pairs of different polymers soluble in organic solvents. In most cases they found demixing and phase separation. Thus out of 35 pairs of polymers tested, only four gave

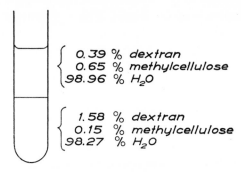

Fig. 2.1. Composition of the two phases formed by a mixture of 1.1 % dextran and 0.36 % methylcellulose in water; see Fig. 2.26.

homogeneous solutions. Experiments on water-soluble polymers by Dobry (14) indicated the same phenomenon. Later studies on polymers in organic solvents (27, 28, 29) and on water-soluble polymers (2) gave additional evidence that this so-called "incompatibility" of polymers is a very general phenomenon.

Further, Dobry & Boyer-Kawenoki (13) found that, in general, if two polymers show "incompatibility" in one solvent they also show it in other solvents. Studies (2, 13) on the effect of the molecular weight of the polymers on the "incompatibility" have shown that this increases if one polymer is replaced by one of greater molecular weight.

In all the systems mentioned above, one polymer collected in one phase and the other in the second phase. A phase separation of a quite different type was described by Pauli & Rona (42, 43), Spiro (52), Tiebackx (56, 57), and Reinders (45). This occurred, for example, if water solutions of gelatin, gum arabic, and acetic acid were mixed in suitable proportions, when it was found that almost all of both polymers collected in one of the phases. This kind of phase separation has been subjected to detailed study for many years by Bungenberg de Jong and his co-workers (7, 9, 10). They found that phase separation occurs only at pH values such that gelatin is positively charged and gum arabic negatively charged. A phase rich in the two polymers is thus formed because of the attraction between the two oppositely charged molecules. Bungenberg de Jong & Kruyt (10) coined the term "coacervation" for the general phenomenon of phase separation of colloid mixtures; for the special case when two oppositely charged polymers collect together in a phase they suggested the name "complex coacervation". Other examples of "complex coacervation" are the combinations gum arabic–haemoglobin and egg albumin–clupein (37) at such pH values that the two colloids have opposite net charges. Further work on phase systems involving oppositely charged polyelectrolytes has been reported by a number of authors. References may be found in a number of books and review articles, for example those of Bungenberg de Jong (9, 10), Booij & Bungenberg de Jong (7), Dervichian (12), and Oparin (37).

So far, we have dealt with systems containing two different polymers and one low molecular component. Liquid phase systems may also be obtained by mixing one polymer with two low molecular components. Thus polyethylene glycol, potassium phosphate, and water in suitable proportions give rise to a liquid two-phase system (2). In this particular case the bottom phase is rich in salt and the top phase rich in polyethylene glycol. Another example is a mixture of dextran, propylalcohol, and water (2). Similar systems have been described by several other workers (7–10, 15, 16, 37, 40).

In the same way, a liquid two-phase system may be obtained by mixing an aqueous solution of a polyelectrolyte with a salt. In this case one of the phases contains most of the polyelectrolyte. Both experimental (10, 18) and theoretical studies (33) have been published on this kind of system and rather specific effects of the ions chosen have been observed. Thus, according to Eisenberg & Ram Mohan (18), salts of polyvinyl sulfonic acid form a two-phase system with NaCl, KCl, and RbCl, but not with LiCl, CsCl, and NH_4Cl. A similar case is shown by a solution of dextran sulfate (see below, page 87), in which a phase separates at room temperature by the addition of KCl and CsCl but not with LiCl, NaCl, and NH_4Cl. In the cold, however, it also forms a two-phase system with NaCl.

The phase systems reported here have been more or less liquid. Frequently one or both of the polymers may precipitate and become converted into a more or less solid phase. Whether a solid or a liquid phase is obtained depends on the specific properties of the polymers and the solvent, and is difficult to predict. For example, dextran forms a liquid phase system with polyethylene glycols with molecular weights above 1000. When lower molecular weight polyethylene glycols are used, dextran is precipitated out in a solid phase. Dextran, ethylalcohol, and water usually give a solid precipitate, whereas if the

14

ethylalcohol is replaced by propylalcohol, a liquid phase is formed.

It has thus been clearly demonstrated that phase separation in a mixture containing one or more polymers often occurs independently of whether the polymer is ionic or not, or whether an organic or aqueous solvent is used. Three kinds of results occur when mixing two different polymer solutions:

1. *"Incompatibility"*, phase separation occurs and the two polymers are collected in different phases.
2. *"Complex coacervation"*, phase separation occurs and the two polymers are collected together in one phase while the other phase consists almost entirely of solvent.
3. *Complete miscibility* when a homogenous solution is obtained. As mentioned above this is the exception rather than the rule in polymer mixtures.

Examples of a number of different aqueous phase systems are given in Table 2.1. They have been classified in two main groups, A and B: Those systems containing two different polymers belong to group A, while those containing only one polymer belong to group B. It is convenient to divide group A further into four subgroups according to whether or not the polymers are charged. Thus group A1 contains only non-ionic polymers; group A2, one non-ionic polymer and one polyelectrolyte (positively or negatively charged); group A3, contains two polyelectrolytes with the same sign of their net charges and group A4, two polyelectrolytes with opposite net charges.

In the same way those systems which belong to group B may be divided into two subgroups. Thus group B1 contains systems with a non-ionic polymer and a non-ionic low molecular component and group B2 contains systems with a polyelectrolyte and a salt.

Any requirement concerning the presence of salt is listed in the third column of Table 2.1.

All systems belonging to the groups A1, A2 and A3 show polymer "incompatibility", i.e. the two polymers go to different phases. As can be seen in Table 2.1, even very closely related and highly hydrophilic compounds may show phase separation when mixed. Such examples are dextran–methylcellulose, dextran sulfate–dextran and the sodium salts of dextran sulfate–carboxymethyldextran. The

15

TABLE 2.1.

List of liquid polymer two-phase systems	With the addition of	Reference

A. *Polymer – polymer – water*

    1. non-ionic polymer (P) – non-ionic polymer (Q) – water

P	Q		
polypropylene glycol	– methoxypolyethylene glycol		
	– polyethylene glycol		2
	– polyvinylalcohol		
	– polyvinylpyrrolidone		2
	– hydroxypropyldextran		
	– dextran		2
polyethylene glycol	– polyvinylalcohol		2
	– polyvinylpyrrolidone		2
	– dextran		2
polyvinylalcohol	– methylcellulose		13
	– hydroxypropyldextran		
	– dextran		2
polyvinylpyrrolidone	– methylcellulose		14
	– dextran		2
methylcellulose	– hydroxypropyldextran		
	– dextran		2
ethylhydroxyethylcellulose	– dextran		2
hydroxypropyldextran	– dextran		

    2. polyelectrolyte (P) – non-ionic polymer (Q) – water

P	Q		
Na dextran sulfate	– polypropylene glycol		
	– methoxypolyethylene glycol	NaCl	
	– polyethylene glycol	NaCl	
	– polyvinylalcohol	NaCl	
	– polyvinylpyrrolidone	NaCl	
	– methylcellulose	NaCl	
	– ethylhydroxyethylcellulose	NaCl	
	– hydroxypropyldextran	NaCl	
	– dextran	NaCl	
Na carboxymethyldextran	– methoxypolyethylene glycol	NaCl	
	– polyethylene glycol	NaCl	
	– polyvinylalcohol	NaCl	
	– polyvinylpyrrolidone	NaCl	
	– methylcellulose	NaCl	
	– ethylhydroxyethylcellulose	NaCl	
	– hydroxypropyldextran	NaCl	

TABLE 2.1. (*cont.*)

List of liquid polymer two-phase systems		With the addition of	Reference
P	*Q*		
Na carboxymethylcellulose	− polypropylene glycol	NaCl	
	− methoxypolyethylene glycol	NaCl	
	− polyethylene glycol	NaCl	
	− polyvinylalcohol	NaCl	
	− polyvinylpyrrolidone	NaCl	
	− methylcellulose	NaCl	
	− ethylhydroxyethylcellulose	NaCl	
	− hydroxypropyldextran	NaCl	
DEAE dextran · HCl	− polypropylene glycol	NaCl	
	− methylcellulose		
	− polyvinylalcohol		

3. polyelectrolyte *(P)* − polyelectrolyte *(Q)* − water; both polyelectrolytes have acid groups

P	*Q*
Na dextran sulfate	− Na carboxymethyldextran
Na dextran sulfate	− Na carboxymethylcellulose
Na carboxymethyldextran	− Na carboxymethylcellulose

4. polyelectrolyte *(P)* − polyelectrolyte *(Q)* − water

P, with acid groups	*Q*, with basic groups	
Na dextran sulfate	− DEAE dextran · HCl	NaCl

B. *Polymer (P) − low molecular weight component (L) − water systems*

P	*L*	
1.		
polypropylene glycol	− potassium phosphate	2
methoxypolyethyleneglycol	− potassium phosphate	2
polyethylene glycol	− potassium phosphate	2
polyvinylpyrrolidone	− potassium phosphate	2
polypropylene glycol	− glucose	2
polypropylene glycol	− glycerol	2
polyvinylalcohol	− butylcellosolve	2
polyvinylpyrrolidone	− butylcellosolve	2
dextran	− butylcellosolve	2
dextran	− propylalcohol	2
2.		
Na dextran sulfate	− sodium chloride (0°C)	

systems which belong to group A4 either show "complex coacervation" i.e. both polymers collect predominantly in one of the phases, while their concentration in the other phase is relatively low, or "incompatibility", i.e. the two polymers go to different phases, depending upon the salt concentration. Thus, when Na dextran sulfate is mixed with diethylaminoethyldextran·HCl at low NaCl concentrations, a phase containing both polymers is obtained, but if the same mixture is made with a high NaCl concentration the first polymer collects in the bottom phase and the second polymer in the top phase. At intermediate NaCl concentrations the two polymers are miscible. This system will be further discussed below (see "Comments on the Phase Systems").

Phase separation in mixtures containing only non-ionic polymers occurs independently of the salt concentration and pH. The systems containing a polyelectrolyte, however, depend very much on the concentration of salts present and the pH, and sometimes phase separation occurs only above certain values of the ionic strength or within certain pH intervals. There is no sharp boundary between the different groups listed in Table 2.1. All possible intermediate systems may be encountered, such as those containing polymers with only a few charged groups. As the degree of substitution is progressively reduced polyelectrolytes will tend to behave as non-ionic polymers.

Those polymer–polymer conbinations, which are possible with the polymers listed here and not found in Table 2.1, either give homogeneous mixtures or a solid precipitate of one of the polymers.

Some of the polymers used here may be regarded as representatives of a whole group of closely related polymers. Thus, in most cases, phase separation is obtained if, for example, in the systems of Table 2.1 dextran is replaced by any of the following polymers: levan, glycogen, soluble starch, and synthetic polyglucose (34), these polymers being mutually compatible. Ionic derivatives of these compounds such as polyglucose sulfate (34) may often replace dextran sulfate and carboxymethyldextran. In the same way methylcellulose and ethyl-hydroxyethylcellulose may be replaced by other water-soluble cellulose derivatives such as ethylcellulose and hydroxyethylcellulose.

Multiphase systems are produced when several polymers, all mutually incompatible, are mixed. A mixture of dextran sulfate, dextran, polyethylene glycol, and polypropylene glycol gives for example a four-phase system.

We will now consider the theoretical basis for this general phenomenon of phase separation among polymer mixtures. In recent years this problem has been studied theoretically by many authors on different kinds of phase systems. By applying modern theories (19, 24, 54) of the thermodynamic properties of polymer solutions, it has been possible to explain at least qualitatively many of the phenomena observed in practice. Systems involving one or more non-ionic polymers have thus been treated by Scott (48) and Tompa (58, 59, 60), and systems involving two oppositely charged polyelectrolytes by Overbeek & Voorn (41) and Voorn (63–67). The results of their investigations are summarized and discussed in the books by Flory (19), and Tompa (60), and in a recent review article by Voorn (68). Only a short account of them will therefore be given here.

Two factors determine the result on mixing two substances. One is the gain in entropy which occurs on mixing the molecules and the other is the interaction between the molecules. The gain in entropy on mixing two substances is related to the *number* of molecules involved in the mixing process. As a first approximation the entropy of mixing is therefore the same for small and large molecules if defined on a *molar* basis. The interaction energy between molecules, however, increases with the *size* of the molecules since it is the sum of the interaction between each small segment of the molecules. Therefore, for very large molecules the interaction energy per mole will tend to dominate over the entropy of mixing per mole. Thus it will be mainly the type of interaction between the molecules which determines the result of mixing two polymers.

Suppose then that the interaction between two unlike polymer molecules is repulsive in character, that is molecules "prefer" to be surrounded by their own kind instead of being mixed. In this case the system will have its energetically most favourable state when the two polymers are separated. The result of mixing solutions of two such polymers is therefore "incompatibility" and there arises one phase which contains the one polymer and another phase with the second polymer. This is the most common result obtained when mixing two polymer solutions; as mentioned above it can occur in mixtures containing non-ionic polymers, polyelectrolytes, or both.

If, on the other hand, the interaction is attractive in character, that is unlike polymer molecules attract each other, then there is a tendency for these to collect together and their separation into a common phase is favoured. This is known as "complex coacervation". The attractive forces necessary for this to occur must be great, however, such as those between oppositely charged polyelectrolytes.

Finally, in the absence of comparatively strong attractive or repulsive forces complete miscibility may result.

In principle there is no difference between the mechanism behind phase separation in a polymer mixture and that in a mixture of low molecular weight substances. We may, for example, compare the "incompatibility" of two polymers with the immiscibility of water and benzene, and "complex coacervation" with the formation of an insoluble inorganic salt like $BaSO_4$. The remarkable point about polymer mixtures is that phase separation takes place even for very closely related polymers and when they are present only in low concentrations of a few per cent.

THE PHASE DIAGRAM

Before we consider the phase systems which in the following have been selected for the fractionation of cell particles and proteins, and which will later be described under "Some Selected Phase Systems", it may be appropriate to discuss a graphical treatment of a phase system, the phase diagram, and experiments by which such diagrams may be derived. Phase diagrams may be constructed in many different ways; only the simplest ones will be described here. For a general treatment on phase diagrams the reader is referred to the books by Treybal (61) and Zernike (69).

In a mixture of two polymers and water, a two-phase system will only arise when the constituents are present in a certain range of proportions. The constituent compositions at which phase separation occurs may be represented in a phase diagram. Figs. 2.2 and 2.3 show such a diagram for a system polymer P–polymer Q–solvent. In Fig. 2.2 the concentration of polymer P is plotted as the abscissa and the concentration of polymer Q as the ordinate; the concentrations are expressed as per cent. The curved line separating two areas is called a *binodial*. All mixtures which have compositions represented by points above the line give rise to phase separation, while mixtures represented by points below the line do not. Thus a composition

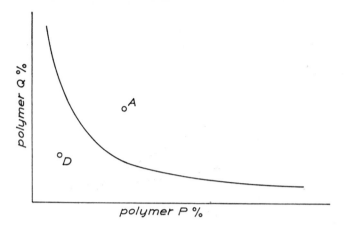

Fig. 2.2. By mixing two polymers P and Q in water, phase separation occurs above certain concentrations of the two polymers, while other mixtures give a homogeneous solution. Thus, mixtures represented by points above the curved line, such as point A, give two liquid phases, while mixtures represented by points below the curved line, such as point D, give one liquid phase. The curved line is called a binodial.

represented by point A in Fig. 2.2 gives a two-phase system, while a composition represented by point D gives a homogenous solution.

In order to describe the two-phase system in more detail, we have also to account for the compositions of the two phases which are in equilibrium. Suppose point A in Fig. 2.3 represents the composition of the total system (per cent of polymer P and Q per total weight mixture). The compositions of the bottom and the top phases obtained with this system will then be represented by points B and C respectively. In the same way, the system with the total composition of A' will have a bottom phase composition of B' and a top phase composition of C'. Like all other points representing the composition of pure phases, points A, B, A', and B' lie on the binodial. Pairs of points like B and C are called *nodes* and the lines joining them are called *tie lines*. Point A, representing the total composition, lies on the tie line joining B and C. Any total composition represented by points on the same tie line will give rise to phase systems with the same phase compositions, but with different volumes of the two phases. If composition is expressed in per cent weight per weight (w/w), the weight ratio bottom phase/top phase is equal to the ratio between the lines AC and AB. This follows from the fact that the weight, m_t, of polymer P in the top

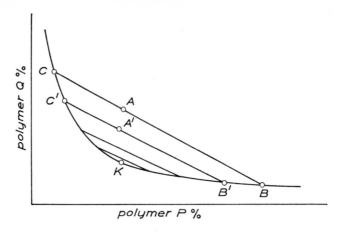

Fig. 2.3. Tie lines, for example the lines BC or $B'C'$, connect the points representing the composition of two phases in equilibrium. Thus, point B represents the composition of the bottom phase, and point C the composition of the top phase of a system with a total composition represented by point A. K is the critical point.

phase plus the weight, m_b, of polymer P in the bottom phase should be equal to the total weight, m_0, of polymer P.

$$m_t + m_b = m_0 \qquad (1)$$

but

$$m_t = V_t \cdot d_t \cdot C_{t/100}, \qquad (2)$$

where V_t is the volume, d_t the density, and C_t the concentration of polymer P in per cent (w/w) of the top phase

and

$$m_b = V_b d_b C_{b/100}, \qquad (3)$$

where V_b is the volume, d_b the density, and C_b the concentration of polymer P in per cent (w/w) of the bottom phase

and

$$m_0 = (V_t d_t + V_b d_b) \cdot C_0, \qquad (4)$$

where C_0 is the total concentration of polymer P in per cent (w/w). Substituting eqns. (2), (3), and (4) in (1) we obtain

$$V_t d_t C_t + V_b d_b C_b = (V_t d_t + V_b d_b) C_0 \qquad (5)$$

or

$$\frac{V_t d_t}{V_b d_b} = \frac{C_b - C_0}{C_0 - C_t} \qquad (6)$$

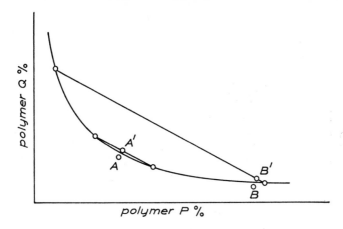

Fig. 2.4. Phase diagram showing the volume ratios obtained for systems near and far away from the critical point, when the composition is changed so that the system shifts from a one-phase to a two-phase system. Point B represents a one-phase system, which by a slight change in composition to point B', is converted to a two-phase system with one small and one large phase. A corresponding shift in composition from A to A' results in a two-phase system with about equal volumes of the phases.

but from the diagram

$$\frac{C_b - C_o}{C_o - C_t} = \frac{\overline{A\,B}}{\overline{A\,C}},$$

hence

$$\frac{V_t d_t}{V_b d_b} = \frac{\overline{A\,B}}{\overline{A\,C}}$$

and

$$\frac{V_t}{V_b} = \frac{d_b}{d_t} \cdot \frac{\overline{A\,B}}{\overline{A\,C}}.$$

The densities of the polymer phases are not very different from that of water (usually in the range between 1.00–1.1) and the ratio of the volumes of the two phases may therefore be obtained approximately from the distances $A\,B$ and $A\,C$ on the tie line.

As may be seen in Fig. 2.3, the more the composition of the phase system approaches point K the difference between the two phases decreases. K is the *critical point* (also called the *plait point*) and the composition represented by point K is called the *critical composition*. At the critical point the compositions and the volumes of the two phases theoretically become equal. Thus a very small change in the total composition from below to above point K means a change from a one-phase system to a two-phase system *with very nearly equal*

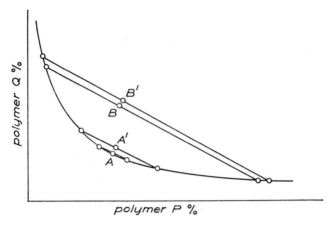

Fig. 2.5. Phase diagram with tie lines showing the sensitivity of a system near the critical composition. A change in the composition of a system from point A to A', which takes place near the critical point, causes a relatively much larger change in the difference between the two phases than a change from B to B', which takes place far away from the critical region.

volumes of the two phases formed. All compositions at the binodial are "critical" in the sense that a small change in composition gives rise to a drastic change in the system, namely from a one-phase system to a two-phase system or *vice versa*, but it is only at the critica lpoint that the volumes of the phases become equal. Fig. 2.4 illustrates this fact as seen from the division of the lines through A' and B'.

It is evident from Fig. 2.5 that near the critical point the property of a two-phase system is most sensitive to changes in its total composition. Compare, for example, the change from A to A' and the change from B to B'. The change from A to A' which occurs near the critical point causes a relatively larger change in the difference between the compositions of the two phases than does the B–B' change.

The same holds for a change in temperature. The two curves in Fig. 2.6 thus represent binodials at two different temperatures. A change in temperature obviously causes a relatively larger change in the difference between the two phases when the composition is near the critical point.

Phase systems near a critical point therefore require more precise experimental control than others and should, if possible, be avoided.

The above considerations apply for ternary systems, i.e. composed of three monodisperse components. Polymers are, however, usually

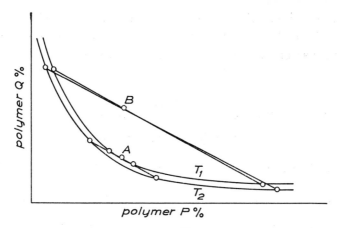

Fig. 2.6. Phase diagram of a system at two different temperatures, T_1 and T_2. A change in the temperature causes a relatively much larger change in the difference between the two phases for a system (A) near the critical composition than for a system (B) removed from the critical composition.

polydisperse, composed of a large number of molecular species with different molecular weights. A system of two polymers and water is therefore not a three component but a multicomponent system. This means that some of the statements given above do not hold strictly for a polymer phase system. We should expect that phase separation from a mixture containing a polydisperse polymer leads to a fractionation of this polymer. Thus in a dextran–polyethylene glycol system, for example, the dextran of the bottom phase has a molecular weight distribution other than the dextran of the top phase (21); the dextran of the bottom phase is therefore not identical with that of the top phase. The statement that "all points on a tie line give the same phase compositions" no longer holds if we are dealing with polydisperse polymers. If in a system of monodisperse polymers we construct the binodial from the mixtures which just give turbidity (see next section) or from the compositions of the phases, two identical lines should be obtained. With polydisperse polymers, however, the two lines may not be identical. The practical significance of these deviations from a strict ternary system will be discussed later (see "Comments on the phase systems").

A phase diagram of polydisperse polymers has, however, a defined critical point. Likewise, the condition that the three points, representing the composition of the total mixture, the top phase, and the bottom phase should lie on a straight line, the tie line, also holds for a system of polydisperse components. This follows from eqns. (1)–(4), which can also be applied to polydisperse systems.

How the Binodial, the Tie Lines and the Critical Point may be Determined Experimentally

A *binodial* may be determined experimentally in one of the following ways:

(*1*) A few grams of a concentrated solution of the one polymer (*P*) are put into a test tube. A solution of known concentration of the other polymer (*Q*) is then added dropwise to the test tube. First a homogeneous mixture is obtained, but after a certain amount of polymer *Q* has been added, one further drop will cause turbidity and a two-phase system will arise. The composition of this mixture is noted. One gram of water is then added and the mixture becomes clear again. More solution of polymer *Q* is then added dropwise until turbidity and a two-phase system is again obtained. The composition of this mixture is noted and more water is added to get a one-phase system and so on. In this way a series of compositions, close to the binodial, are obtained and, if the concentration of polymer *P* is plotted against that of *Q* for these compositions, a line as that of Fig. 2.2 is obtained.

When the polymers are polydisperse, as is usually the case, there is not a sharp change from a clear solution to a turbid mixture, particularly when one of the polymers is present at a low concentration. By adding polymer *Q* a very weak turbidity first appears probably because only the largest molecules of polymer *P* separate into a phase. Then as more of polymer *Q* is added, more polymer *P* separates out and the turbidity increases. For very polydisperse polymers this method is therefore rather tedious.

(*2*) The compositions of the phases of a number of different systems are determined and a curve, the binodial, is drawn through the points representing these compositions.

The *tie lines* are obtained by analyzing the composition of each phase. This gives points *B* and *C* of Fig. 2.3 and the tie line is that joining these points. Alternatively, only one phase may be analyzed. If the total composition and the ratio between the weights of the two

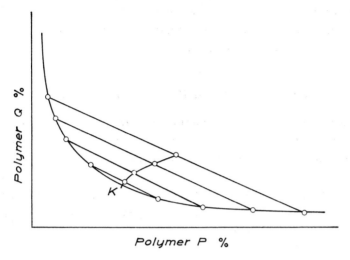

Fig. 2.7. Phase diagram showing how the critical point K may be obtained by extrapolation. A line is drawn through the middle points of the tie lines and intersects the curved line, i.e. the binodial, at the critical point.

phases are known, the composition of the other phase may be obtained by calculation according to eqn. (6).

The *critical point* is determined in one of the two following ways.

(*1*) By trial and error a mixture is made such that, after the addition of a drop of the one polymer solution, conversion from a one-phase to a two-phase system with equal volumes of the phases occurs.

(*2*) If tie lines have been determined near the critical point, a line is drawn through the middle points of these and extrapolated to the binodial. The critical point lies, approximately, where this line intersects the binodial, see Fig. 2.7.

SOME SELECTED PHASE SYSTEMS

The phase systems which have been selected and used for the fractionation of particles and macromolecules have been analyzed in more detail and are listed in Table 2.4. These systems were chosen mainly because they have not too high viscosities, or too long separation times for the phases. In addition the polymers used are relatively inert, well defined, and available commercially in large amounts. Below follows a description of the polymers, how their solutions are made and the different phase systems analyzed. Finally, the results and the properties of the systems will be summarized and discussed.

The Polymers and Polymer Solutions

In general, it is a good rule always to standardize the procedure for making a polymer solution, since the property of such solution may sometimes depend on its previous history.

Dextran[1] (*D*). All the dextran fractions used were supplied by Pharmacia, Uppsala, Sweden. The chemistry of dextran and its application in medicine has been treated in two monographs by Squire, Bull, Maycock & Ricketts (53) and Grönwall (23), where many references may be found. Dextran is a branched polyglucose built up by the bacterium *Leuconostoc mesenteroides* when it grows on appropriate solutions of sucrose. After isolation and partial acid hydrolysis, different fractions are obtained by differential alcohol precipitation, and subsequently purified. Each fraction is characterized by the manufacturer, using the limiting viscosity number $[\eta]$, number average molecular weight $\bar{M}_n$, and weight average molecular weight $\bar{M}_w$. The fractions which have been used here are given in Table 2.2. The greater the quotient $\bar{M}_w/\bar{M}_n$, the more polydisperse is the fraction. The physico-chemical properties of these various fractions have been investigated by Granath (20).

The glucose units of the main chain in a dextran molecule are mainly connected by 1→6 linkages. The branches are connected with this chain through 1→3 linkages. For the dextran used here about 94 per cent of the linkages are 1→6 linkages, the rest being 1→3 linkages (3, 51). It has a specific optical rotation of $[\alpha]_D^{25} = +199°$, if the $\bar{M}_n$ value exceeds about 10,000.

The dextran used contained 5–10 per cent moisture. Solutions were originally prepared from dextran dried at 120° for 12 hours. It was found, however, that drying by heat occasionally caused a brown-yellow colour change and an increase in absorption of ultraviolet light. Solutions were therefore prepared directly from the undried

---

[1] I am indebted to Drs. P. Flodin and K. Granath for valuable information on the properties of dextran and its derivatives.

TABLE 2.2. *Data of various dextran fractions (according to the manufacturer).*

Abbreviation used in this book	Limiting viscosity number[a] ml/g	Number average molecular weight M_n	Weight average molecular weight M_w
D 5	4.5	2 300	3 400
D 17	16.8	23 000	~30 000
D 19	19	20 000	42 000
D 24	24	40 500	
D 37	37	83 000	179 000
D 48	48	180 000	460 000
D 68	68	280 000	2 200 000
D 70	70	73 000	—

[a] The same as intrinsic viscosity which is usually expressed in dl/g.

dextran and the concentration of the solution was determined by polarimetry. The procedure is as follows. The undried dextran is first wetted and mixed to a paste with a small amount of water. The rest of the water is then added and the dextran dissolved by stirring and slowly heating the mixture to boiling. The solution is then allowed to cool down with the flask covered by a watch glass. For the determination of the concentration, about 10 g of the solution are weighed into a 25 ml measuring flask, which is then filled to the mark with water. The optical rotation of this solution is then determined in a polarimeter using a tube 20 cm long. For stock solutions, 10–20 per cent (w/w) is a suitable concentration range for the higher molecular weight dextrans and 20–30 per cent (w/w) for the lower molecular weight dextrans.

In experiments where it was desirable to have as low UV absorption as possible, the dextran was reduced and precipitated by alcohol in the following way (53). A 10 per cent solution of dextran is first prepared as above. 6 mg $NaBH_4$ are then added per gram of dextran. During reduction the pH rises and this is counteracted by the addition of HCl. When the reduction is complete (no further increase in pH), the solution is added dropwise to a 95 per cent alcohol solution with vigorous stirring; the alcohol concentration should never fall below 80 per cent. The precipitate is collected and dried in air. Dextran treated in this way may be dissolved directly in cold water. The UV spectra of such a solution, after filtration through a Jena glass filter No. 3G4, is given in Fig. 2.8.

Dextran solutions, except those of the low molecular weight fractions are stable if kept under sterile conditions. The low molecular weight fractions such as D 5 and D 17 undergo crystallization after some time and give rise to milky solutions. These may, however, be clarified by heating up to boiling.

Concentrated solutions of D 5 do not become clear if dissolved as above, and must therefore be clarified by filtration. Their concentration has been determined by dry weight determination since the $[\alpha]_D^{25}$ value used for the other fractions, does not apply to D 5.

Hydroxypropyldextran (*HPD*), was obtained from Pharmacia, Uppsala, Sweden. It had been prepared from a dextran fraction with a limiting viscosity number of 70 ml/g. Its degree of substitution was approximately 1 per glucose unit. It may be dissolved directly in water and the concentration determined by dry weight determination.

Carboxymethyldextran, sodium salt (*NaCMD*), was obtained from Pharmacia, Uppsala, Sweden. The fraction which was used had been prepared from a dextran fraction with a limiting viscosity number of 68 ml/g. Its equivalent weight was 297. The product was dissolved in water, filtered, dialyzed against water, freeze dried, and kept over P_2O_5.

Dextran sulfate, sodium salt (*NaDS*), was supplied by Pharmacia, Uppsala, Sweden. Two samples were used which had been prepared from dextran fractions with the limiting viscosity numbers of 70 ml/g and 68 ml/g respectively. They will be referred to as NaDS 70 and NaDS 68 respectively. Its sulfur content was 16.8 per cent. It was dried and kept over P_2O_5 and used without further purification. The specific optical rotation for dextran sulfate varies slightly with the salt concentration. $[\alpha]_D^{21}$ was found to be $+100°$ in water, $+99.6°$ in 0.15 M NaCl, $+99.5°$ in 0.3 M NaCl, and $+98.9°$ in 1 M NaCl.

Diethylaminoethyl dextran, chloride form (*DEAE dextran · HCl*) (35), was obtained from Pharmacia, Uppsala, Sweden. It had been prepared from a dextran fraction with a limiting viscosity number of 68 ml/g. Its equivalent weight was 1630. (Flodin, personal communication.)

Methylcellulose (*MC*) was obtained from the Dow Chemical Company, U.S.A. Three different products were used: "Methocel 4000",

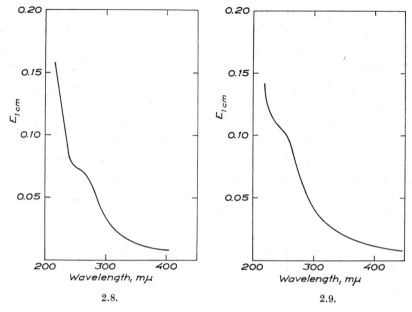

Fig. 2.8. Absorption curve for a 10 % (w/w) solution of dextran (D48).

Fig. 2.9. Absorption curve for a 1 % (w/w) solution of methylcellulose (MC4000).

"Methocel 400", and "Methocel 10", all U.S.P. grades. They will be referred to as MC4000, MC400, and MC10 respectively. The figures indicate viscosity in centipoises of a 2 per cent solution. Data on the properties of Methocel may be obtained from Methocel Handbook (32), published by the Dow Chemical Company. Information about the chemistry of cellulose ethers in general may be obtained from ref. (62). From data on the degree of polymerization as a function of the viscosity of a 2 per cent solution (22), MC4000 may be calculated to have a mean molecular weight of about 140000, MC400 about 80000, and MC10 about 30000. These values are, however, somewhat uncertain and the fractions are rather polydisperse. 1–2, 5, and 10 per cent (w/w) are suitable concentrations for stock solutions of MC4000, 400, and 10 respectively. The methylcellulose was dried at 110°C for 24 hours. 1 kg of a 1 per cent (w/w) solution of MC4000 is prepared in the following way. 10 g of dry methylcellulose are weighed into an Erlenmeyer flask and 300–500 ml hot (80–90°C) water added. The flask is closed and shaken vigorously for a few minutes in order to wet the powder. 500 ml cold water are then added, the flask shaken and allowed to stand with occasional stirring until it reaches room temperature. The powder now swells and is slowly dissolved; but, note well, it should not be allowed to sediment to the bottom of the flask. The flask is put on the balance and water added to bring it to the desired weight. The solution is then cooled down to 4°C and kept at this temperature before use. The concentration is checked by dry weight determination at 110°C. The final cooling down of the solution is necessary in order to get a clear solution. Since the solution properties, for example viscosity, of cellulose ethers in general depend on the lowest temperature to which they have been subjected (25), all solutions are cooled down to the same temperature. An absorption curve of methylcellulose is shown in Fig. 2.9.

Carboxymethylcellulose, sodium salt (NaCMC) was obtained from Uddeholms Ltd., Sweden. It was dissolved directly in water to a 2 per cent w/w solution.

Ethyl hydroxyethylcellulose (EHEC) was supplied by Mo och Domsjö, Ltd., Örnsköldsvik, Sweden, with the trade name "Modocoll". Its properties are described in papers by Jullander (25, 26) and Manley (30). A sample designated Modocoll E 600 was used. It was dissolved directly in water, cooled down to 4°C and before use it was clarified by centrifugation. This product is rather polydisperse (31) with a weight average molecular weight of about 200000.

Polyvinylalcohol (PVA) was obtained from Firma Wacker Chemie, GMBH, Munich, Germany. It is marketed under the trade name "Polyviol". The following products were used: Polyviol 48/20 and 28/20. They will be referred to as PVA 48/20 and PVA 28/20 respectively. A solution of polyvinylalcohol is prepared by first wetting the powder with hot water to a paste and then adding the rest of the water and keeping the mixture at 100°C until a solution is obtained. The concentration is determined by dry weight determination.

Polyethylene glycol (PEG) was obtained in the form of "Carbowax" compounds produced by Carbide and Carbon Chemicals Company, U.S.A. The samples used are described in Table 2.3. Information on the properties of polyethylene glycol may be found in ref. (11). Polyethylene glycol is dissolved directly in water and the concentration

TABLE 2.3. *Samples of polyethylene glycols which have been used.*

Abbreviation used in this book	Commercial name: "Carbowax" polyethylene glycol	Number average molecular weight (11)
PEG 20 000	20 M	15 000–20 000
PEG 6 000	6 000	6 000– 7 500
PEG 4 000	4 000	3 000– 3 700
PEG 1 540	1 540	1 300– 1 600
PEG 1 000	1 000	950– 1 050
PEG 600	600	570– 630
PEG 400	400	380– 420
PEG 300	300	285– 315

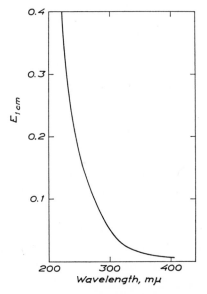

Fig. 2.10. Absorption curve for a 10 % (w/w) solution of purified polyethylene glycol (PEG 6000).

is determined by freeze drying. (Dry weight determination by heating is unsatisfactory because part of the polyethylene glycol evaporates and during drying a cake is formed which may retain much water.) The "Carbowax" compounds contain small amounts of an impurity which has a peak of absorption in UV light at 290 mμ (31). This may be removed by precipitation of the polyethylene glycol from an acetone solution with ether. Such a purification of PEG 6000 is done in the following way. 300 g PEG 6000 are dissolved by careful warming in

6 l acetone, 3 l ether are then added during stirring. The mixture is allowed to stand overnight. The precipitate is collected by filtration through a filter paper, washed with an acetone–ether (2:1) mixture and dried in air. The UV spectrum of such a preparation is given in Fig.2.10.

Polypropylene glycol (*PPG*) was obtained from the Carbide and Carbon Chemicals Company, U.S.A., with the name "Polypropylene glycol 425" and had an average molecular weight of 400–500 (10).

Methoxy polyethylene glycol (*MPEG*) was obtained as "Carbowax methoxy polyethylene glycol 550" from the Carbide and Carbon Chemicals Company, U.S.A. It had an average molecular weight of 525–575 (10).

Analysis of the Phases

For most of the phase systems the compositions of the different phases were calculated from determinations of the water content and the concentration of one of the polymers; the concentration of the other polymer is then obtained by subtraction. The total composition is always known since the phase systems are set up by mixing weighed amounts of water and polymer solutions with known concentrations. Thus the compositions of the total system, the top phase, and the bottom phase are usually determined in each experiment. The condition that these three compositions can be represented by three points on a straight line, see Fig. 2.3, in the phase diagram, is thus a check on the accuracy of the analysis.

The phase systems are prepared in the following way. Suitable amounts of water and polymer solutions are weighed into a separating funnel. Because of their high viscosity, polymer solutions are measured by weight instead of volume. This may be conveniently done on an automatic balance (Mettler, type K7). The funnel is equilibrated in a thermostat and the contents mixed by inverting the funnel about 50 times. The funnel is then allowed to stand for 24–48 hours for phase separation. Samples from the top phase are taken by a pipette and from the bottom phase through the outlet of the funnel. The samples are then analyzed as follows.

The dextran–polyethylene glycol system. For dry weight determination samples of about 3–5 g from each phase were weighed into wide 50 ml weighing glasses or 100 ml Erlenmeyer flasks, diluted with 10–20 ml water and freeze dried. After freeze drying the samples were further dried over P_2O_5 to constant weight; this latter drying was necessary since dextran, which retains water rather firmly, was not always dried completely by freeze drying. For dextran determinations samples of about 10 g from each phase were weighed into 25 ml measuring flasks which were then filled with water. The dextran concentration was then determined using a polarimeter and tubes 20 cm long.

In some experiments the drying of the bottom phase was not satisfactory. In these cases the point representing the bottom phase composition was obtained from the intersection of the line joining the points representing the top phase and the total compositions and the line representing the dextran concentration of the bottom phase.

The dextran–polyvinylalcohol system was analysed in a similar way to the dextran–polyethylene glycol system.

The dextran–methylcellulose system. For dry weight determinations 10–15 g samples were kept at 110°C for 48 hours. Dextran was determined polarimetrically on another sample. Methylcellulose exhibits a small optical rotation and is therefore removed before dextran is determined. This was done by adding 5 g 30 per cent (w/w) $(NH_4)_2SO_4$ to a sample of about 10 g of the phase. This precipitated the methylcellulose, which could then be removed by filtration through a Pyrex glass filter, marked S.F.1A1 or S.F.1A2. (Filter paper was unsatisfactory.) The filtrate was collected in a 25 ml measuring flask. The precipitate was washed with 10 per cent (w/w) $(NH_4)_2SO_4$ and the flask filled with water. The dextran concentration was then determined polarimetrically.

The dextran–ethylhydroxyethylcellulose system was analysed in a similar way to the dextran–methylcellulose system.

The dextran–hydroxypropyldextran system. For dry weight determinations samples of about 5 g were kept at 110°C for 24–48 hours.

Dextran was determined polarimetrically on another sample. Hydroxy-propyldextran exhibits optical rotation and is therefore removed before the dextran is determined. This was done by adding ammonium sulfate up to 25 per cent (w/w). The precipitate was removed by filtration through a glass filter (Pyrex, marked S.F.1A1 or S.F.1A2) or by centrifugation.

The Na dextran sulfate–polyethylene glycol–sodium chloride system. The dry weight was determined in the same way as for the dextran-polyethylene glycol system. The Na dextran sulfate was determined polarimetrically in a similar manner to dextran in the dextran-polyethylene glycol system. The phase system analysed contained 0.3 M NaCl and the dextran sulfate has an $[\alpha]_D^{21}$ value of $+99.5°$ (see above). The sodium chloride content of each phase was obtained by passing a sample through a Dowex 50 column in acid form. The liberated acid was determined by titration using methyl blue–methyl red as indicator. Part of the liberated acid is dextran sulfuric acid and its equimolar content has therefore to be subtracted. It was calculated from the per cent (w/w) content of the phase as determined polarimetrically and its equivalent weight; this latter was determined to be 209 by passing a known solution of dialysed Na dextran sulfate through a Dowex 50 column. Thus the dry weight, the sodium chloride, and the Na dextran sulfate contents are known. The polyethylene glycol content is then obtained by subtraction.

The Na dextran sulfate–methylcellulose–sodium chloride system. Dry weight was determined by freeze drying since dextran sulfate cannot be heated for a long time. The Na dextran sulfate was deter-mined polarimetrically after the methylcellulose had been precipitated and removed as described for the dextran–methylcellulose system. The Na dextran sulfate solution thus obtained contains 10 per cent (w/w) ammonium sulfate and has an $[\alpha]_D^{21}$ value of $+100°$. Sodium chloride distributes almost equally between the two phases and its concentration in each phase was therefore considered to be 0.15 and 0.3 M respectively for the two systems studied, see Figs. 2.35 and 2.36. The methylcellulose concentration was then obtained by sub-tracting the sodium chloride and the Na dextran sulfate concentrations from the dry weight. In some experiments the drying of the bottom phase was unsatisfactory and in these cases the point representing the bottom phase was obtained from the intersection of the line joining the points representing the top phase and the total compositions and the line representing the Na dextran sulfate concentration of the bottom phase.

The Na dextran sulfate–polyvinylalcohol–sodium chloride system was analysed in the same way as the Na dextran sulfate–methylcellulose–sodium chloride system; the sodium chloride concentration was considered to be 0.3 *M* in both phases since it distributes almost equally between the phases, see Fig. 2.37.

The potassium phosphate–polyethylene glycol systems were analysed in the following way. 2–6 g samples were freeze dried as described for the dextran–polyethylene glycol system. The dried samples were then dissolved in water and passed through a column of the acid form of Dowex 50. The liberated phosphoric acid was then titrated with 0.1 *M* NaOH using bromcresol green as indicator. In this way the salt can be determined and the polyethylene glycol concentration is obtained by subtraction.

PHASE DIAGRAMS

The results of the analysis of the selected systems listed in Table 2.4 are given in Figs. 2.11–2.48. As a convention, the concentration of the polymer which distributes in favour of the bottom phase is plotted as abscissa, and the concentration of the polymer which distributes in favour of the top phase is plotted as the ordinate. The composition of the phases and the total system are recorded under each phase diagram. The systems are listed in alphabetical order, this being the same as the order of their distances from the critical point. The potassium phosphate used was a mixture with the following ratio: 306.9 g K_2HPO_4 to 168.6 g KH_2PO_4.

TABLE 2.4.

Selected phase systems analyzed	Figs. showing phase diagram
Dextran – polyethylene glycol – water	2.11–2.25
Dextran – methylcellulose – water	2.26–2.29
Dextran – polyvinylalcohol – water	2.30–2.31
Dextran – hydroxypropyldextran – water	2.32
Na dextran sulfate – polyethylene glycol – sodium chloride – water	2.33–2.34
Na dextran sulfate – methylcellulose – sodium chloride – water	2.35–2.36
Na dextran sulfate – polyvinylalcohol – sodium chloride – water	2.37
Na carboxymethyldextran – polyethylene glycol – sodium chloride – water	2.38
Potassium phosphate – polyethylene glycol – water	2.39–2.45
Potassium phosphate – methoxypolyethylene glycol – water	2.46
Potassium phosphate – polypropylene glycol – water	2.46
Ammonium sulfate – polyethylene glycol – water	2.47
Magnesium sulfate – polyethylene glycol – water	2.48

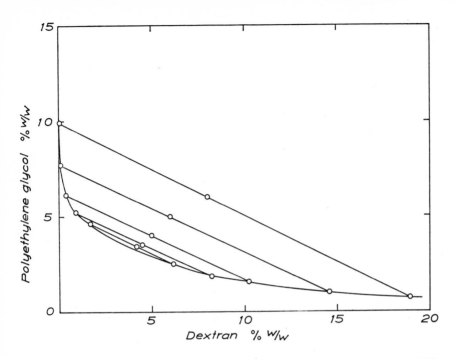

Sys-tem	Total system			Bottom phase			Top phase		
	Dextran % w/w	Poly-ethylene glycol % w/w	H$_2$O % w/w	Dextran % w/w	Poly-ethylene glycol % w/w	H$_2$O % w/w	Dextran % w/w	Poly-ethylene glycol % w/w	H$_2$O % w/w
A	4.20	3.40	92.40	6.14	2.50	91.36	1.72	4.62	93.66
B	4.50	3.50	92.00	8.22	1.83	89.95	0.90	5.22	93.88
C	5.00	4.00	91.00	10.20	1.55	88.25	0.36	6.13	93.51
D	6.00	5.00	89.00	14.59	0.98	84.43	0.11	7.71	92.18
E	8.00	6.00	86.00	18.93	0.70	80.37	0.05	9.88	90.07

Fig. 2.11 Phase diagram and phase compositions of the dextran–polyethylene glycol system D 68 – PEG 6000 at 20°C.

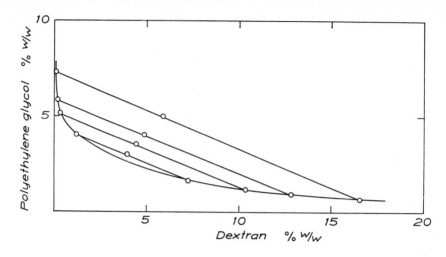

Sys-tem	Total system			Bottom phase			Top phase		
	Dextran % w/w	Poly-ethylene glycol % w/w	H₂O % w/w	Dextran % w/w	Poly-ethylene glycol % w/w	H₂O % w/w	Dextran % w/w	Poly-ethylene glycol % w/w	H₂O % w/w
A	3.92	3.00	93.08	7.23	1.64	91.13	1.20	4.02	94.78
B	4.41	3.51	92.08	10.37	1.19	88.44	0.26	5.14	94.60
C	4.89	4.00	91.11	12.82	0.91	86.27	0.16	5.83	94.01
D	5.87	5.00	89.13	16.52	0.67	82.81	0.07	7.29	92.64

Fig. 2.12. Phase diagram and phase compositions of the dextran–polyethylene glycol system D 68 – PEG 6000 at 0°C.

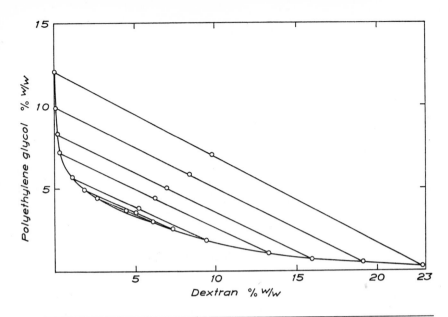

| Sys-tem | Total system | | | Bottom phase | | | Top phase | | |
	Dextran % w/w	Poly-ethylene glycol % w/w	H₂O % w/w	Dextran % w/w	Poly-ethylene glycol % w/w	H₂O % w/w	Dextran % w/w	Poly-ethylene glycol % w/w	H₂O % w/w
A	4.40	3.65	91.95	6.10	2.98	90.92	2.63	4.43	92 94
B	5.00	3.50	91.50	7.34	2.55	90.11	1.80	4.91	93.29
C	5.20	3.80	91.00	9.46	1.85	88.69	1.05	5.70	93.25
D	6.20	4.40	89.40	13.25	1.07	85.68	0.30	7.17	92.53
E	7.00	5.00	88.00	15.89	0.68	83.43	0.14	8.29	91.57
F	8.40	5.80	85.80	19.08	0.52	80.40	0.06	9.93	90.01
G	9.80	7.00	83.20	22.77	0.24	76.99	0.05	12.03	87.92

Fig. 2.13. Phase diagram and phase compositions of the dextran–polyethylene glycol system D 48 – PEG 6000 at 20°C.

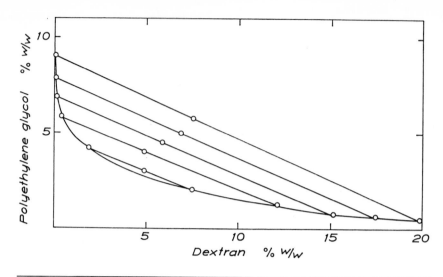

Sys-tem	Total system Dextran % w/w	Poly-ethylene glycol % w/w	H$_2$O % w/w	Bottom phase Dextran % w/w	Poly-ethylene glycol % w/w	H$_2$O % w/w	Top phase Dextran % w/w	Poly-ethylene glycol % w/w	H$_2$O % w/w
A	4.89	3.00	92.11	7.50	2.03	90.47	1.87	4.20	93.93
B	4.89	4.00	91.11	12.13	1.28	86.59	0.36	5.84	93.80
C	5.86	4.50	89.64	15.13	0.79	84.08	0.13	6.90	92.97
D	6.84	5.00	88.16	17.48	0.67	81.85	0.06	7.89	92.05
E	7.52	5.77	86.71	19.93	0.55	79.52	0.03	9.03	90.94

Fig. 2.14. Phase diagram and phase compositions of the dextran–polyethylene glycol system D 48 – PEG 6000 at 0°C.

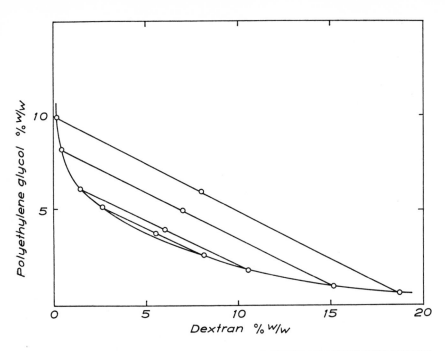

Sys-tem	Total system			Bottom phase			Top phase		
	Dextran % w/w	Poly-ethylene glycol % w/w	H$_2$O % w/w	Dextran % w/w	Poly-ethylene glycol % w/w	H$_2$O % w/w	Dextran % w/w	Poly-ethylene glycol % w/w	H$_2$O % w/w
A	5.50	3.80	90.70	8.10	2.67	89.23	2.62	5.20	92.18
B	6.00	4.00	90.00	10.50	1.85	87.65	1.43	6.18	92.39
C	7.00	5.00	88.00	15.17	0.96	83.87	0.41	8.24	91.35
D	8.00	6.00	86.00	18.68	0.63	80.69	0.16	9.96	89.88

Fig. 2.15. Phase diagram and phase compositions of the dextran–polyethylene glycol system D 37 – PEG 6000 at 20°C.

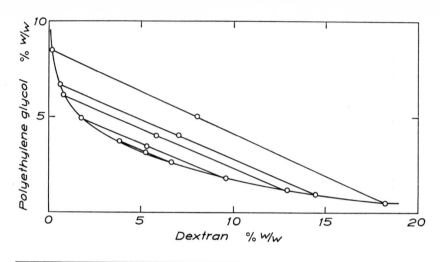

Sys-tem	Total system			Bottom phase			Top phase		
	Dextran % w/w	Poly-ethylene glycol % w/w	H$_2$O % w/w	Dextran % w/w	Poly-ethylene glycol % w/w	H$_2$O % w/w	Dextran % w/w	Poly-ethylene glycol % w/w	H$_2$O % w/w
A	5.24	3.13	91.63	6.67	2.66	90.67	3.84	3.73	92.43
B	5.30	3.44	91.26	9.56	1.80	88.64	1.74	4.91	93.35
C	5.82	4.00	90.18	12.94	1.20	85.86	0.72	6.11	93.17
D	7.02	4.02	88.96	14.45	0.95	84.60	0.61	6.69	92.70
E	8.02	5.00	86.98	18.21	0.50	81.29	0.15	8.50	91.35

Fig. 2.16. Phase diagram and phase compositions of the dextran–polyethylene glycol system D 37 – PEG 6000 at 0°C.

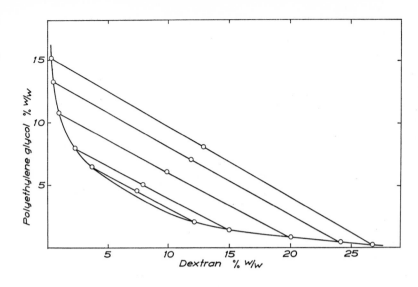

Sys-tem	Total system			Bottom phase			Top phase		
	Dextran % w/w	Poly-ethylene glycol % w/w	H$_2$O % w/w	Dextran % w/w	Poly-ethylene glycol % w/w	H$_2$O % w/w	Dextran % w/w	Poly-ethylene glycol % w/w	H$_2$O % w/w
A	7.39	4.52	88.09	12.13	2.04	85.83	3.62	6.46	89.92
B	7.89	5.02	87.09	14.96	1.40	83.64	2.25	7.94	89.81
C	9.87	6.03	84.10	20.01	0.85	79.14	0.93	10.75	88.32
D	11.84	7.04	81.12	24.10	0.43	75.47	0.43	13.25	86.32
E	12.83	8.04	79.13	26.72	0.22	73.06	0.27	15.11	84.62

Fig. 2.17. Phase diagram and phase compositions of the dextran–polyethylene glycol system D 24 – PEG 6000 at 20°C.

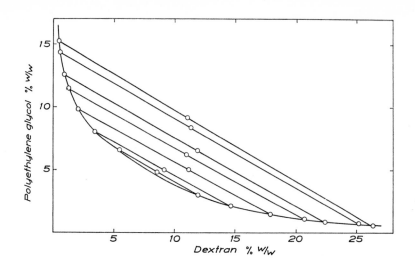

Sys-tem	Total system			Bottom phase			Top phase		
	Dextran % w/w	Poly-ethylene glycol % w/w	H₂O % w/w	Dextran % w/w	Poly-ethylene glycol % w/w	H₂O % w/w	Dextran % w/w	Poly-ethylene glycol % w/w	H₂O % w/w
A	8.54	4.77	86.69	11.91	3.00	85.09	5.41	6.59	88.00
B	9.14	5.00	85.86	14.67	2.10	83.23	3.41	8.02	88.57
C	11.18	5.00	83.82	17.89	1.46	80.65	2.01	9.80	88.19
D	10.98	6.22	82.80	20.69	1.12	78.19	1.22	11.47	87.31
E	11.87	6.51	81.62	22.38	0.85	76.77	0.89	12.55	86.56
F	11.33	8.35	80.32	25.17	0.78	74.05	0.55	14.37	85.08
G	11.05	9.16	79.79	26.40	0.50	73.10	0.41	15.21	84.38

Fig. 2.18. Phase diagram and phase compositions of the dextran–polyethylene glycol system D 17 – PEG 6000 at 20°C.

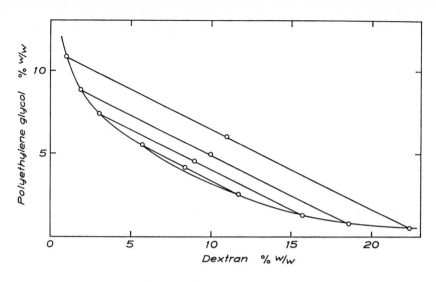

Sys-tem	Total system			Bottom phase			Top phase		
	Dextran % w/w	Poly-ethylene glycol % w/w	H₂O % w/w	Dextran % w/w	Poly-ethylene glycol % w/w	H₂O % w/w	Dextran % w/w	Poly-ethylene glycol % w/w	H₂O % w/w
A	8.31	4.15	87.54	11.66	2.55	85.79	5.70	5.55	88.75
B	8.92	4.58	86.50	15.71	1.30	82.99	3.01	7.42	89.57
C	9.92	4.97	85.11	18.56	0.80	80.64	1.85	8.85	89.30
D	10.93	6.02	83.05	22.32	0.55	77.13	0.99	10.81	88.20

Fig. 2.19. Phase diagram and phase compositions of the dextran–polyethylene glycol system D 17 – PEG 6000 at 0°C.

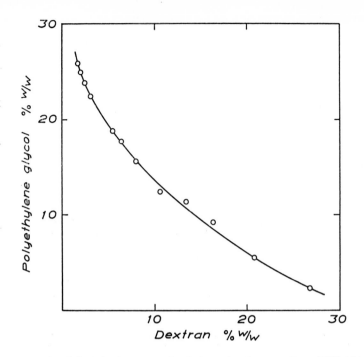

Fig. 2.20. Binodial of the dextran–polyethylene glycol system D 5 – PEG 6000 at 20°C.

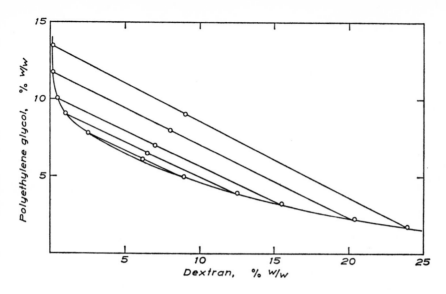

	Total system			Bottom phase			Top phase		
Sys-tem	Dextran % w/w	Poly-ethylene glycol % w/w	H$_2$O % w/w	Dextran % w/w	Poly-ethylene glycol % w/w	H$_2$O % w/w	Dextran % w/w	Poly-ethylene glycol % w/w	H$_2$O % w/w
A	6.14	6.09	87.77	8.91	4.99	86.10	2.52	7.82	89.66
B	6.50	6.50	87.00	12.48	3.93	83.59	1.00	9.09	89.91
C	7.00	7.00	86.00	15.50	3.25	81.25	0.44	10.07	89.49
D	8.00	8.00	84.00	20.34	2.28	77.38	0.15	11.80	88.05
E	9.00	9.00	82.00	23.81	1.90	74.29	0.13	13.46	86.41

Fig. 2.21. Phase diagram and phase compositions of the dextran-polyethylene glycol system D 48 – PEG 4000 at 20°C.

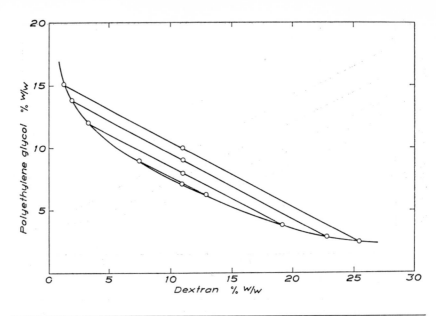

Sys-tem	Total system			Bottom phase			Top phase		
	Dextran % w/w	Poly-ethylene glycol % w/w	H$_2$O % w/w	Dextran % w/w	Poly-ethylene glycol % w/w	H$_2$O % w/w	Dextran % w/w	Poly-ethylene glycol % w/w	H$_2$O % w/w
A	10.94	7.12	81.94	12.88	6.29	80.83	7.46	8.99	83.55
B	11.04	7.97	80.99	19.14	3.90	76.96	3.25	12.01	84.74
C	11.06	9.00	79.94	22.80	2.89	74.31	1.90	13.82	84.28
D	11.00	10.00	79.00	25.45	2.32	72.23	1.28	15.18	83.54

Fig. 2.22. Phase diagram and phase compositions of the dextran–polyethylene glycol system D 17 – PEG 4000 at 20°C.

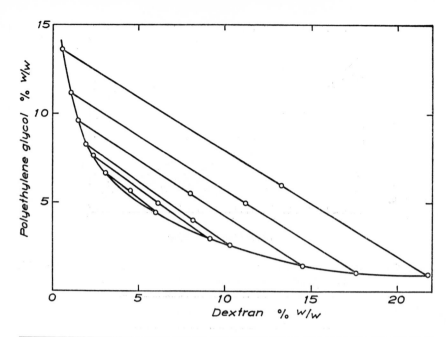

Sys-tem	Total system			Bottom phase			Top phase		
	Dextran % w/w	Poly-ethylene glycol % w/w	H₂O % w/w	Dextran % w/w	Poly-ethylene glycol % w/w	H₂O % w/w	Dextran % w/w	Poly-ethylene glycol % w/w	H₂O % w/w
A	4.51	5.65	89.84	6.00	4.39	89.61	3.05	6.63	90.32
B	4.98	6.10	88.92	9.19	2.97	87.84	2.32	7.62	90.06
C	3.98	8.14	87.88	10.32	2.55	87.13	1.87	8.27	89.86
D	8.00	5.50	86.50	14.47	2.33	83.20	1.44	9.65	88.91
E	4.98	11.18	83.84	17.60	1.05	81.35	1.04	11.17	87.79
F	5.98	13.22	80.80	21.79	0.97	77.24	0.53	13.65	85.82

Fig. 2.23. Phase diagram and phase compositions of the dextran–polyethylene glycol system D 17 – PEG 20 000 at 20°C.

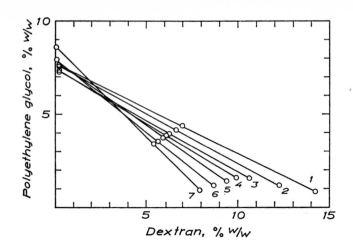

Fig. 2.24. Tie lines of the dextran–polyethylene glycol system D 48 – PEG 6000 with the addition of various amounts of NaCl, at 20°C.

Line number	moles of NaCl[a]
1	0.1
2	1.0
3	2.0
4	2.5
5	3.0
6	4.0
7	5.0

[a] added to 1 kg of the system 7 % (w/w) D 48; 4.4 % (w/w) PEG 6000; 88.6 % (w/w) H_2O.

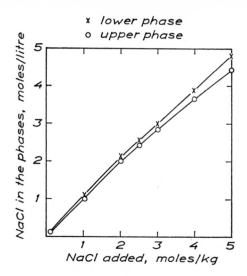

Fig. 2.25. Partition of NaCl in the dextran–polyethylene glycol system D 48 – PEG 6000. *Abscissa:* molar concentration of NaCl in the phases. *Ordinata:* moles of NaCl added to 1 kg of the system 7 % (w/w) D 48; 4.4 % (w/w) PEG 6000; 88.6 % (w/w) H_2O, at 20°C.

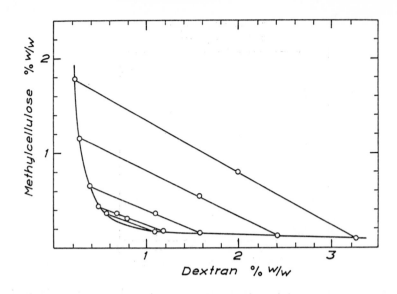

Sys-tem	Total system			Bottom phase			Top phase		
	Dextran % w/w	Methyl-cellu-lose % w/w	H$_2$O % w/w	Dextran % w/w	Methyl-cellu-lose % w/w	H$_2$O % w/w	Dextran % w/w	Methyl-cellu-lose % w/w	H$_2$O % w/w
A	0.79	0.30	98.91	1.09	0.17	98.74	0.57	0.36	99.07
A 1	0.68	0.36	98.96	1.18	0.17	98.65	0.47	0.43	99.10
B	1.10	0.36	98.54	1.58	0.15	98.27	0.39	0.65	98.96
C	1.58	0.54	97.88	2.42	0.12	97.46	0.28	1.15	98.57
D	2.00	0.80	97.20	3.27	0.10	96.63	0.23	1.78	97.99

Fig. 2.26. Phase diagram and phase compositions of the dextran–methylcellulose system D 68 – MC 4000 at 20°C.

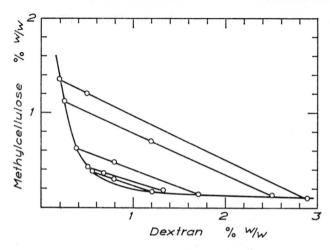

Sys-tem	Total system			Bottom phase			Top phase		
	Dextran % w/w	Methyl-cellu-lose % w/w	H₂O % w/w	Dextran % w/w	Methyl-cellu-lose % w/w	H₂O % w/w	Dextran % w/w	Methyl-cellu-lose % w/w	H₂O % w/w
A	0.80	0.30	98.90	1.21	0.17	98.62	0.56	0.38	99.06
A 1	0.68	0.36	98.96	1.33	0.18	98.49	0.51	0.43	99.06
B	0.80	0.48	98.72	1.72	0.14	98.14	0.38	0.63	98.99
C	1.20	0.70	98.10	2.51	0.14	97.35	0.25	1.12	98.63
D	0.50	1.20	98.30	2.88	0.09	97.03	0.18	1.37	98.45

Fig. 2.27. Phase diagram and phase compositions of the dextran–methylcellulose system D 68 – MC 4000 at 4°C.

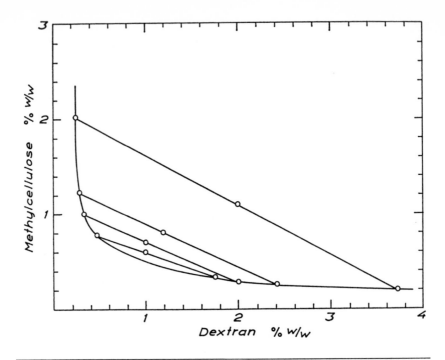

	Total system			Bottom phase			Top phase		
Sys-tem	Dextran % w/w	Methyl-cellu-lose % w/w	H_2O % w/w	Dextran % w/w	Methyl-cellu-lose % w/w	H_2O % w/w	Dextran % w/w	Methyl-cellu-lose % w/w	H_2O % w/w
A	1.00	0.60	98.40	1.76	0.33	97.91	0.47	0.78	98.75
B	1.00	0.70	98.30	2.01	0.29	97.70	0.33	1.00	98.67
C	1.20	0.80	98.00	2.42	0.26	97.32	0.28	1.23	98.49
D	2.00	1.10	96.90	3.74	0.20	96.06	0.24	2.02	97.74

Fig. 2.28. Phase diagram and phase compositions of the dextran–methylcellulose system D 68 – MC 400 at 20°C.

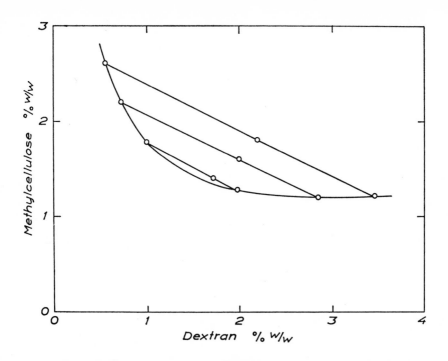

Sys-tem	Total system			Bottom phase			Top phase		
	Dextran % w/w	Methyl-cellu-lose % w/w	H₂O % w/w	Dextran % w/w	Methyl-cellu-lose % w/w	H₂O % w/w	Dextran % w/w	Methyl-cellu-lose % w/w	H₂O % w/w
A	1.72	1.40	96.88	1.98	1.29	96.73	1.00	1.78	97.22
B	2.00	1.60	96.40	2.85	1.20	95.95	0.73	2.20	97.07
C	2.20	1.80	96.00	3.45	1.22	95.33	0.55	2.61	96.84

Fig. 2.29. Phase diagram and phase compositions of the dextran–methylcellulose system D 68 – MC 10 at 20°C.

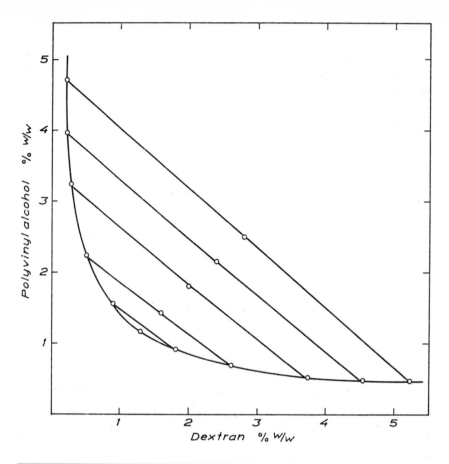

	Total system			Bottom phase			Top phase		
Sys-tem	Dextran % w/w	Poly-vinyl-alcohol % w/w	H₂O % w/w	Dextran % w/w	Poly-vinyl-alcohol % w/w	H₂O % w/w	Dextran % w/w	Poly-vinyl-alcohol % w/w	H₂O % w/w
A	1.30	1.16	97.54	1.81	0.92	97.27	0.91	1.56	97.53
B	1.60	1.42	96.98	2.61	0.68	96.71	0.50	2.23	97.27
C	2.00	1.78	96.22	3.74	0.53	95.73	0.28	3.25	96.47
D	2.40	2.14	95.46	4.55	0.48	94.97	0.21	3.99	95.80
E	2.80	2.49	94.71	5.23	0.47	94.30	0.20	4.69	95.11

Fig. 2.30. Phase diagram and phase compositions of the dextran–polyvinylalcohol system D 68 – PVA 48/20 at 20°C.

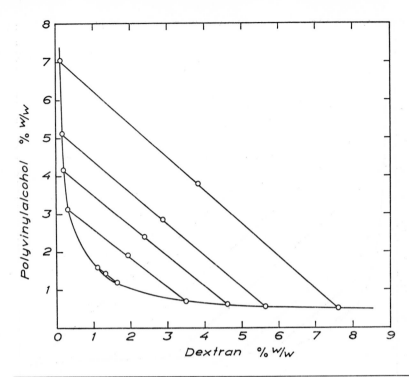

Sys-tem	Total system			Bottom phase			Top phase		
	Dextran % w/w	Poly-vinyl-alcohol % w/w	H_2O % w/w	Dextran % w/w	Poly-vinyl-alcohol % w/w	H_2O % w/w	Dextran % w/w	Poly-vinyl-alcohol % w/w	H_2O % w/w
A	1.34	1.44	97.22	1.65	1.19	97.16	1.11	1.59	97.30
B	1.91	1.90	96.19	3.49	0.69	95.82	0.31	3.13	96.56
C	2.39	2.38	95.23	4.60	0.61	94.79	0.18	4.16	95.66
D	2.87	2.85	94.28	5.64	0.55	93.81	0.16	5.11	94.73
E	3.82	3.80	92.38	7.60	0.53	91.87	0.12	7.06	92.82

Fig. 2.31. Phase diagram and phase compositions of the dextran–polyvinylalcohol system D 68 – PVA 28/20 at 20°C.

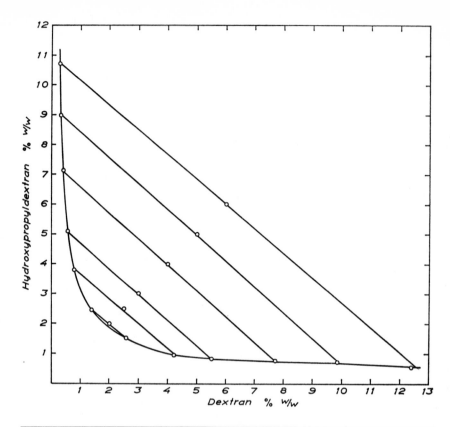

	Total system			Bottom phase			Top phase		
System	Dextran % w/w	Hydroxy-propyl-dextran % w/w	H₂O % w/w	Dextran % w/w	Hydroxy-propyl-dextran % w/w	H₂O % w/w	Dextran % w/w	Hyproxy-propyl-dextran % w/w	H₂O % w/w
A	2.00	2.00	96.00	2.56	1.52	95.92	1.37	2.47	96.16
B	2.50	2.50	95.00	4.20	0.95	94.85	0.77	3.78	95.45
C	3.00	3.00	94.00	5.51	0.82	93.67	0.56	5.19	94.25
D	4.00	4.00	92.00	7.72	0.75	91.53	0.39	7.13	92.48
E	5.00	5.00	90.00	9.88	0.72	89.40	0.29	8.96	90.75
F	6.00	6.00	88.00	12.38	0.51	87.11	0.24	10.67	89.09

Fig. 2.32. Phase diagram and phase compositions of the dextran–hydroxypropyldextran system D 68 – HPD 70 at 4°C.

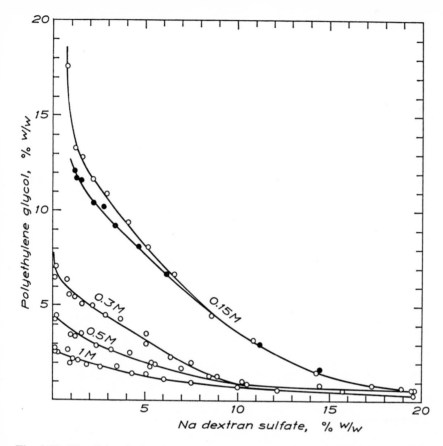

Fig. 2.33. Binodials of the Na dextran sulfate–polyethylene glycol system NaDS 68 – PEG 6000 at various NaCl concentrations (expressed as moles per litre phase system). ○, 20°C, ●, 4°C.

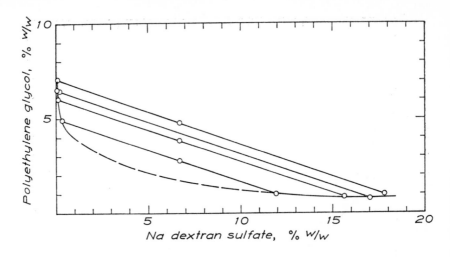

System	Total system		Bottom phase		Top phase	
	Na dextran sulfate % w/w	Poly- ethylene glycol % w/w	Na dextran sulfate % w/w	Poly- ethylene glycol % w/w	Na dextran sulfate % w/w	Poly- ethylene glycol % w/w
A	6.69	2.87	11.88	1.0	0.31	4.91
B	6.67	3.81	15.59	0.8	0.08	6.02
C	0.20	6.45	17.01	0.8	0.01	6.5
D	6.67	4.76	17.79	1.0	0.03	7.03

Fig. 2.34. Phase diagram and polymer compositions of the Na dextran sulfate–poly-ethylene glycol system NaDS 68 – PEG 6000 in 0.3 M NaCl at 4°C.

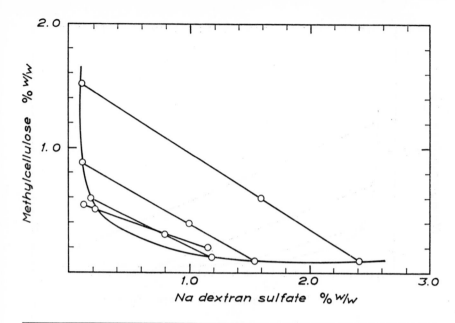

	Total system		Bottom phase		Top phase	
	Na dextran sulfate % w/w	Methyl-cellu-lose % w/w	Na dextran sulfate % w/w	Methyl-cellu-lose % w/w	Na dextran sulfate % w/w	Methyl-cellu-lose % w/w
System						
A	0.22	0.51	1.15	0.20	0.13	0.54
B	0.80	0.30	1.19	0.13	0.18	0.59
C	1.00	0.40	1.55	0.10	0.11	0.88
D	1.60	0.60	2.42	0.09	0.11	1.52

Fig. 2.35. Phase diagram and polymer compositions of the Na dextran sulfate–methylcellulose system NaDS 68 – MC 4000 in 0.15 M NaCl at 4°C.

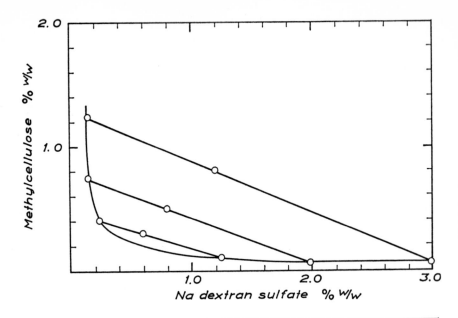

System	Total system		Bottom phase		Top phase	
	Na dextran sulfate % w/w	Methyl-cellu-lose % w/w	Na dextran sulfate % w/w	Methyl-cellu-lose % w/w	Na dextran sulfate % w/w	Methyl-cellu-lose % w/w
A	0.60	0.30	1.25	0.11	0.24	0.41
B	0.80	0.50	1.99	0.06	0.14	0.75
C	1.20	0.80	3.00	0.06	0.15	1.24

Fig. 2.36. Phase diagram and polymer compositions of the Na dextran sulfate–methylcellulose system NaDS 68 – MC 4000 in 0.3 M NaCl at 4°C.

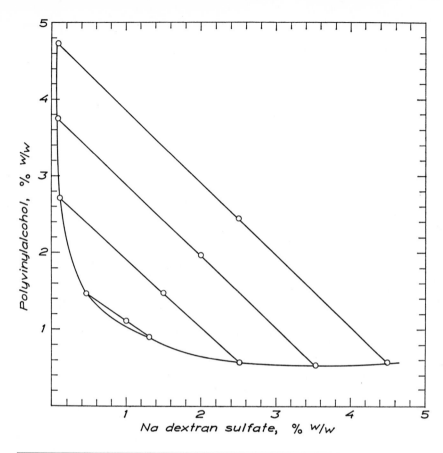

System	Total system		Bottom phase		Top phase	
	Na dextran sulfate % w/w	Poly-vinyl-alcohol % w/w	Na dextran sulfate % w/w	Poly-vinyl-alcohol % w/w	Na dextran sulfate % w/w	Poly-vinyl-alcohol % w/w
A	1.00	1.11	1.31	0.90	0.45	1.47
B	1.50	1.47	2.51	0.57	0.10	2.71
C	2.00	1.96	3.53	0.54	0.08	3.75
D	2.50	2.44	4.49	0.57	0.08	4.73

Fig. 2.37. Phase diagram and polymer compositions of the phases of the Na dextran sulfate–polyvinylalcohol system NaDS 68 – PVA 48/20 in 0.15 NaCl at 4°C.

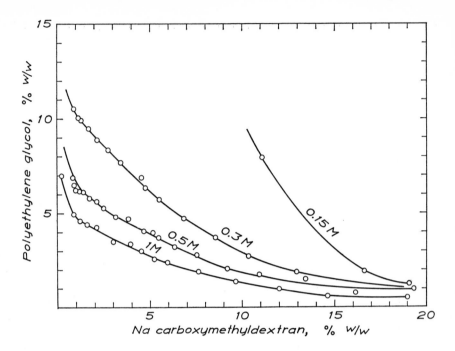

Fig. 2.38. Binodials of the Na carboxymethyldextran–polyethylene glycol system NaCMD 68 – PEG 6000 at various NaCl concentrations at 20°C.

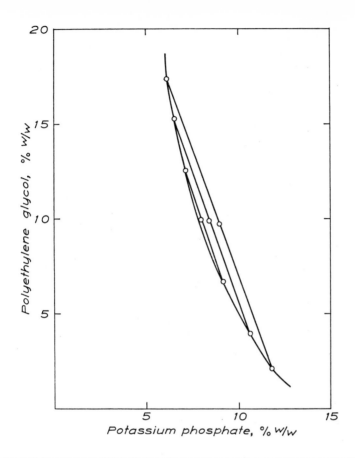

Sys-tem	Total system			Bottom phase			Top phase		
	Potassium phosphate % w/w	Polyethylene glycol % w/w	H₂O % w/w	Potassium phosphate % w/w	Polyethylene glycol % w/w	H₂O % w/w	Potassium phosphate % w/w	Polyethylene glycol % w/w	H₂O % w/w
A	7.92	10.04	82.04	9.13	6.68	84.19	7.13	12.57	80.30
B	8.36	9.91	81.73	10.57	3.95	85.48	6.52	15.25	78.23
C	8.94	9.69	81.37	11.74	2.08	86.18	6.11	17.36	76.53

Fig. 2.39. Phase diagram and phase compositions of the potassium phosphate – PEG 20 000 system at 20°C.

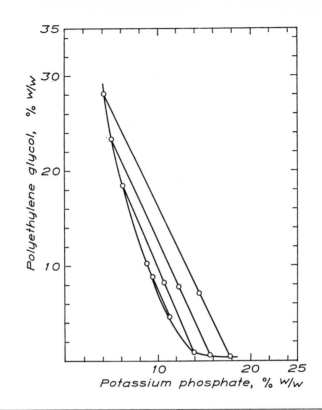

Sys-tem	Total system			Bottom phase			Top phase		
	Potas-sium phos-phate % w/w	Poly-ethylene glycol % w/w	H_2O % w/w	Potas-sium phos-phate % w/w	Poly-ethylene glycol % w/w	H_2O % w/w	Potas-sium phos-phate % w/w	Poly-ethylene glycol % w/w	H_2O % w/w
A	9.37	8.79	81.84	11.17	4.65	84.18	8.76	10.20	81.04
B	10.65	8.26	81.09	13.84	0.90	85.26	6.13	18.45	75.42
C	12.17	7.79	80.04	15.53	0.55	83.92	5.03	23.28	71.69
D	14.37	7.04	78.59	17.66	0.37	81.97	4.13	28.00	67.87

Fig. 2.40. Phase diagram and phase compositions of the potassium phosphate – PEG 6000 system at 20°C.

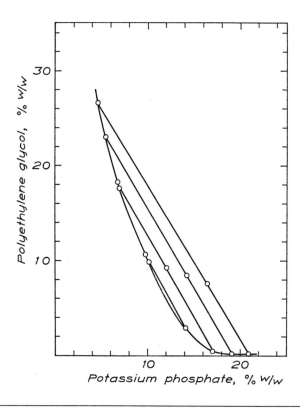

Sys-tem	Total system			Bottom phase			Top phase		
	Potas-sium phos-phate % w/w	Poly-ethylene glycol % w/w	H₂O % w/w	Potas-sium phos-phate % w/w	Poly-ethylene glycol % w/w	H₂O % w/w	Potas-sium phos-phate % w/w	Poly-ethylene glycol % w/w	H₂O % w/w
A	10.16	9.92	79.92	13.99	2.94	83.07	9.74	10.63	79.63
B	12.02	9.20	78.78	17.01	0.50	82.49	6.70	18.26	75.04
C	14.17	8.39	77.44	19.00	0.19	80.81	5.46	23.03	71.51
D	16.38	7.55	76.07	20.87	0.18	78.95	4.60	26.57	68.83

Fig. 2.41. Phase diagram and phase compositions of the potassium phosphate – PEG 6000 system at 0°C.

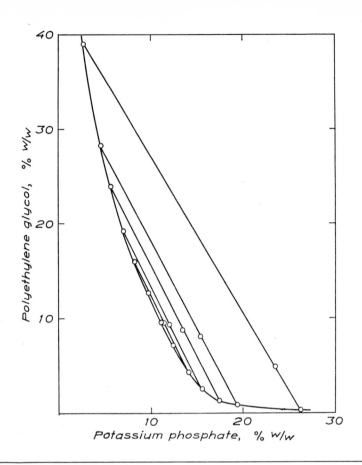

	Total system			Bottom phase			Top phase		
System	Potassium phosphate % w/w	Polyethylene glycol % w/w	H₂O % w/w	Potassium phosphate % w/w	Polyethylene glycol % w/w	H₂O % w/w	Potassium phosphate % w/w	Polyethylene glycol % w/w	H₂O % w/w
A	11.04	9.55	79.41	12.35	7.09	80.56	9.67	12.65	77.68
B	11.37	9.42	79.21	14.06	4.23	81.71	8.19	15.96	75.85
C	11.97	9.19	78.84	15.46	2.54	82.00	7.01	19.16	73.83
D	13.36	8.67	77.97	17.41	1.30	81.29	5.56	23.90	70.54
E	15.30	7.93	76.77	19.41	0.78	79.81	4.55	28.15	67.30
F	23.37	4.87	71.76	26.26	1.01	72.73	2.68	38.92	58.40

Fig. 2.42. Phase diagram and phase compositions of the potassium phosphate – PEG 4000 system at 20°C.

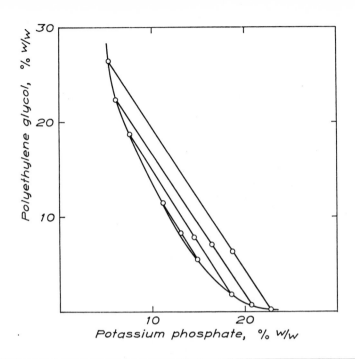

Sys-tem	Total system			Bottom phase			Top phase		
	Potas-sium phos-phate % w/w	Poly-ethylene glycol % w/w	H₂O % w/w	Potas-sium phos-phate % w/w	Poly-ethylene glycol % w/w	H₂O % w/w	Potas-sium phos-phate % w/w	Poly-ethylene glycol % w/w	H₂O % w/w
A	13.11	8.23	78.66	14.87	5.48	79.65	11.13	11.44	77.43
B	14.54	7.74	77.72	18.57	1.72	79.71	7.63	18.66	73.71
C	16.51	7.02	76.47	20.67	0.63	78.70	5.98	22.29	71.73
D	18.63	6.30	75.07	22.73	0.14	77.13	5.29	26.33	68.38

Fig. 2.43. Phase diagram and phase compositions of the potassium phosphate – PEG 4000 system at 0°C.

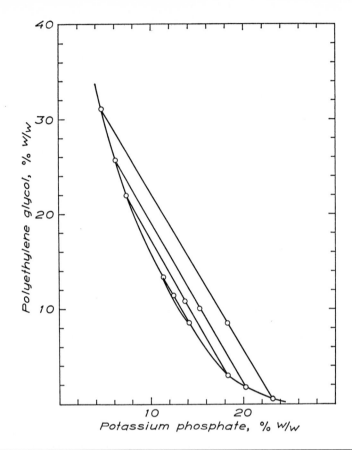

Sys-tem	Total system			Bottom phase			Top phase		
	Potassium phosphate % w/w	Polyethylene glycol % w/w	H$_2$O % w/w	Potassium phosphate % w/w	Polyethylene glycol % w/w	H$_2$O % w/w	Potassium phosphate % w/w	Polyethylene glycol % w/w	H$_2$O % w/w
A	12.36	11.37	76.27	14.12	8.57	77.31	11.35	13.38	75.27
B	13.66	10.74	75.60	18.34	2.94	78.72	7.31	21.86	70.83
C	15.21	9.99	74.80	20.13	1.68	78.19	6.11	25.64	68.25
D	18.13	8.56	73.31	23.17	0.48	76.35	4.62	31.00	64.38

Fig. 2.44. Phase diagram and phase compositions of the potassium phosphate – PEG 1540 system at 20°C.

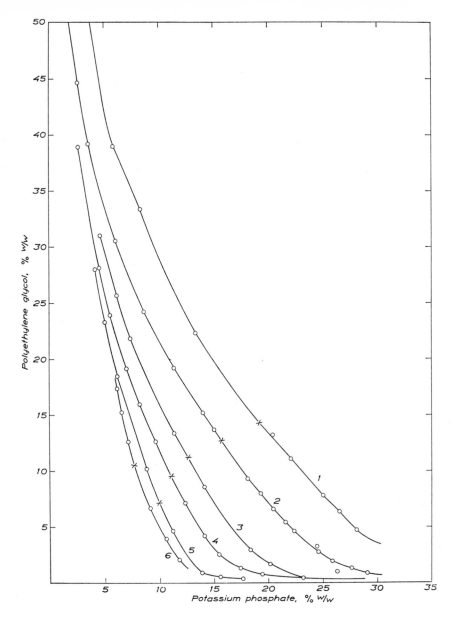

Fig. 2.45. Binodials and critical points (×) of potassium phosphate–polyethylene glycol systems at 20°C with the following polyethylene glycol fractions:

1	PEG 300	4	PEG 4000
2	PEG 600	5	PEG 6000
3	PEG 1540	6	PEG 20 000

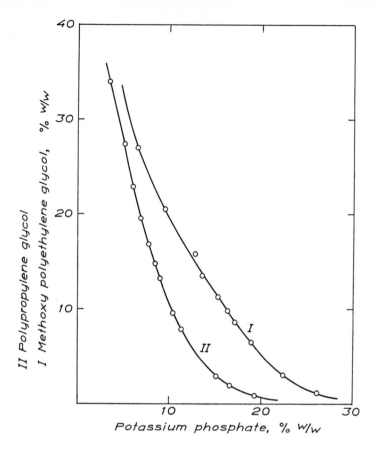

Fig. 2.46. Binodials of the systems potassium phosphate–methoxypolyethylene glycol (I), and potassium phosphate–polypropylene glycol (II) at 20°C.

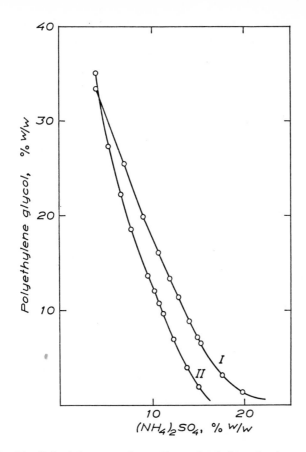

Fig. 2.47. Binodials of the ammonium sulfate–polyethylene glycol systems $(NH_4)_2SO_4$–PEG 1540 (I) and $(NH_4)_2SO_4$–PEG 4000 (II) at 20°C.

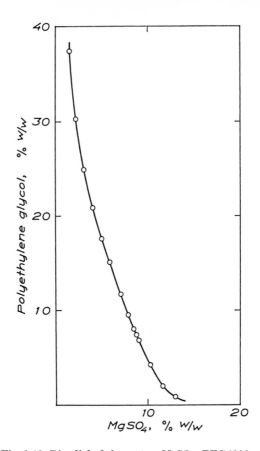

Fig. 2.48. Binodial of the system $MgSO_4$–PEG 4000 at 20°C.

COMMENTS ON THE PHASE SYSTEMS

Influence of Molecular Weight of the Polymers

In Figs. 2.49 and 2.50 the phase diagrams for the different polymer fractions are compared. As may be seen from these figures, the higher the molecular weight of the polymers, the lower the concentration required for phase separation, and the larger the difference

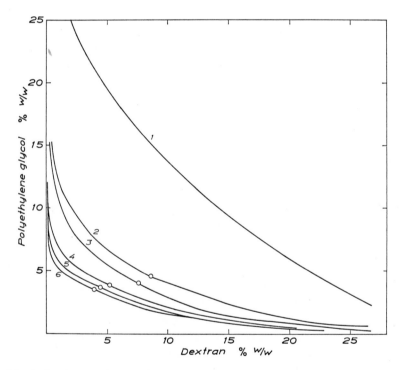

Fig. 2.49. Binodials and critical points ($\bigcirc$) of dextran–polyethylene glycol systems with the same polyethylene glycol (PEG 6000) and with the following fractions of dextran:

1	D 5 ($\overline{M}_n = 2300$	$\overline{M}_w = 3400$)
2	D 17 ($\overline{M}_n = 23\,000$	$\overline{M}_w = 30\,000$)
3	D 24 ($\overline{M}_n = 40\,500$	—)
4	D 37 ($\overline{M}_n = 83\,000$	$\overline{M}_w = 179\,000$)
5	D 48 ($\overline{M}_n = 180\,000$	$\overline{M}_w = 460\,000$)
6	D 68 ($\overline{M}_n = 280\,000$	$\overline{M}_w = 2\,200\,000$)

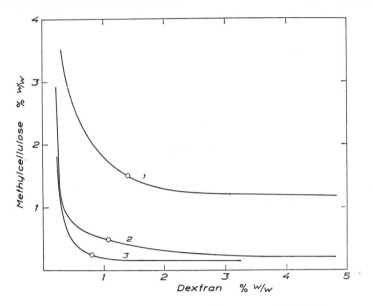

Fig. 2.50. Binodials and critical points (○) of dextran–methylcellulose systems with the same dextran fraction (D 68) and with the following methylcellulose fractions: *1*. MC 10, *2*. MC 400, *3*. MC 4000.

in molecular size between the two polymers, the more asymmetrical is the binodial. Qualitatively the diagrams in Figs. 2.49 and 2.50 are in good agreement with what might be expected from theory (48, 60).

The Viscosity

Generally it might be expected that, the higher the molecular weight of the polymers used, the higher the viscosity of the phases. This is true in many cases. This increase in viscosity due to greater molecular weight is, however, partly compensated for by the fact that lower concentrations of polymers with larger molecular weights are required for phase separation. Since the viscosity of a polymer solution is greatly dependent on concentration, this opposing effect may sometimes be considerable. The viscosity of one of the phases may thus be reduced by using a higher molecular weight fraction of the polymer which collects in the other phase. This is illustrated by the following example of the dextran–methylcellulose system. Phase systems of

78

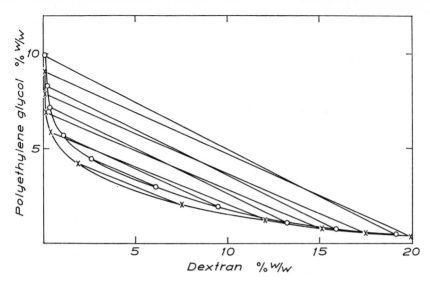

Fig. 2.51. Phase diagram of the dextran–polyethylene glycol system D48–PEG6000 at 20°C (○), and 0°C (×).

MC4000 and D24, D37, or D48 have very viscous top phases (the methylcellulose rich phases) and are too viscous to be used for practical purposes. By using D68, however, one may use so low a concentration of MC4000 that a more suitable phase system is obtained.

The dextran–polyethyleneglycol, dextran sulfate–polyethyleneglycol, and salt–polyethylene glycol systems have convenient viscosities. The most viscous systems are those containing methylcellulose and polyvinylalcohol. The molecules of the latter substances have a linear chain structure and, for a given molecular weight and concentration, such molecules give rise to solutions with higher viscosities than solutions of branched molecules such as dextran. More or less compact molecules are the most suitable as far as viscosity is concerned. A sphere would be the ideal form of the molecules since the viscosity of a suspension of spherical particles does not depend on the size of the particles but only on their volume fraction (17). By increasing the molecular weight, a lower volume fraction would be necessary for phase separation, and therefore lower viscosity could be obtained.

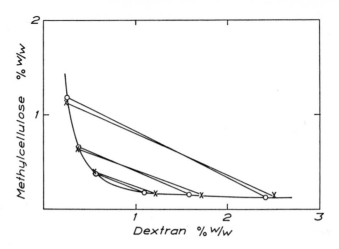

Fig. 2.52. Phase diagram of the dextran–methylcellulose system D 68–MC 4000 at 20°C (○), and 4°C (×).

Influence of Temperature

Phase diagrams of the dextran–polyethylene glycol and the dextran–methylcellulose systems at different temperatures are shown in Figs. 2.51 and 2.52 respectively. The dextran–polyethylene glycol system can separate into phases with lower polymer concentrations at lower temperatures, while the dextran–methylcellulose system is hardly affected by changes in temperature. The differences in temperature sensitivity of systems with compositions close or far away from the critical point have already been pointed out (page 24).

The Time of Phase Separation

The time required for the phases to separate varies considerably for the different systems. It depends not only on the difference in density between the two phases and their viscosities, but also on the time needed for the small droplets, formed during shaking, to coalesce into larger drops. Near the critical point the density difference is small and the settling time therefore long. Far away from the critical point the polymer concentration and therefore the viscosity are high,

80

TABLE 2.5. *Approximate times of phase separation for different polymer two-phase systems.*

Phase system	Time
salt – polyethylene glycol	5–15 min
dextran – polyethylene glycol	5–60 min
dextran sulfate – polyethylene glycol	5–60 min
dextran – methylcellulose	1–12 hrs
dextran sulfate – methylcellulose	1–12 hrs
dextran – polyvinylalcohol	$\frac{1}{2}$– 6 hrs
dextran sulfate – polyvinylalcohol	$\frac{1}{2}$– 6 hrs
dextran – hydroxypropyldextran	$\frac{1}{2}$– 6 hrs
dextran sulfate – hydroxypropyldextran	$\frac{1}{2}$– 6 hrs

so that the settling time also becomes long for such systems. Thus at intermediate compositions the settling time is the shortest.

The times of phase separation for a number of systems are recorded in Table 2.5.

In a given phase system the settling time also depends on the volume ratio of the two phases if these have different viscosities. If the more viscous phase is larger in volume than the other phase, the settling time is longer than if the more viscous phase has a volume about equal to or smaller than the other phase. This holds, for example, for the dextran–polyethylene glycol system where the top phase is less viscous than the bottom phase. When the bottom phase is the larger in volume these systems separate more slowly than when the phases have equal volumes or the top phase is larger.

If a test tube containing a two–phase mixture very close to the critical point is shaken, and allowed to stand, one can then immediately observe that the mixture appears almost clear, as though it were a one-phase system. Cloudiness appears a few seconds later, indicating the formation of a two-phase system. Apparently the drops of the two phases, due to the extremely low interfacial tension, are broken down by the shaking and dispersed to such an extent that their dimensions are of the same order as the molecules. The mixture may then be regarded as being almost a one-phase system. This "reversal" of phase separation by mechanical mixing has been studied quantitatively by Silberberg & Kuhn (50). They subjected a two-phase system to shear at a steady and uniform rate and studied the size and shapes of the droplets of the one phase in the other. It was found that at a certain critical rate of shear the droplets disappeared and the system became homogeneous. The phenomenon was reversible. The period during which the solution is optically clear immediately after mixing the phases is longer the closer the mixture lies to the critical composition. This is to be expected since the interfacial tension becomes smaller for systems closer to the critical points. It is also longer for the dextran–methylcellulose system than for the other systems.

The times given in Table 2.5 are those required for the main bulk of the phases to separate i.e. until a horizontal interface has been formed. Usually small drops of one phase remain in the other for a long time after the horizontal interface is apparent. The amount of this emulsification varies considerably for different phase systems and depends also on the volume ratio. For liquid phase systems in general it is a common experience that there is less emulsification in the smallest phase; in fact a transparent phase may be obtained if it is very small compared with the other phase (Fig. 2.53). Thus, the bottom phase of the system dextran–polyethylene glycol, with a volume less than one-tenth of the total volume, is almost optically clear. The large top phase then contains an emulsion. In the same way the top phase can be made clear by reducing its volume. This effect is at least partly due to the fact that it is only the smallest phase which, for geometrical reasons, can form drops in the other phase. Emulsification is, however, a rather complicated phenomenon which depends on many factors. The reader is referred to standard books on surface chemistry (1, 6) for a general treatment of emulsions.

Finally, Figs. 7.4–7 (Chapter 7) demonstrate how the phase separation of some systems proceeds as a function of time. All these systems had a small bottom phase whose volume was recorded at different times after the shaking of the tubes. As is shown in these figures, we may distinguish three parts to each curve. The first part, where no phase has yet appeared at the bottom of the tube, indicates that during this "lag" period the small drops are being formed and are coalescing into larger drops. These then become so large that they can sediment by their own weight, which takes place in the second period where the curve is almost a straight line. The end of this period means that

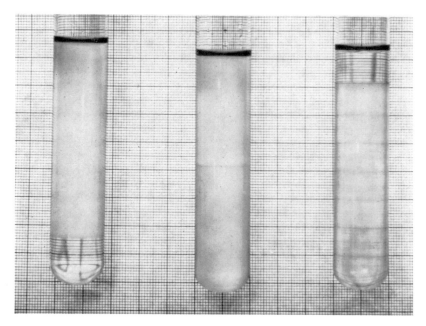

Fig. 2.53. Influence of the volume ratio on emulsions in the phases of a dextran–polyethylene glycol system. *Left*: the volume of the bottom phase is about 1/10 of that of the top phase; *middle*: the two phases have about equal volumes; and *right*: the volume of the top phase is about 1/10 of that of the bottom phase. The bottom phase (*left*) and the top phase (*right*) are clear, while the other phases are turbid.

the main bulk of the phases has separated and a horizontal interface has been established. In the last period, the remaining volume of the bottom phase comes down as very slowly sedimenting droplets.

The Density of the Phases

The densities of the phases may be calculated approximately from their polymer compositions and the densities of known polymer solutions which are recorded in Tables 2.6–2.11.

The Interfacial Tension

No measurements of the liquid–liquid interfacial tension have been made on the phase systems described here. From data (15, 47, 49) on other polymer–polymer two-phase systems, one would expect small values in the range of 0.001–0.1 dyne/cm, for the interfacial tension. It also seems reasonable that the dextran–methylcellulose system has a lower interfacial tension than the dextran–polyethylene glycol system, since the first system has a much smaller difference in composition between the two phases.

TABLE 2.6. *Density of aqueous solutions of dextran (D 48) at 20°C.*

Polymer concentration, % (w/w)	d_4^{20}
1.0	1.001
2.0	1.005
3.0	1.009
4.0	1.013
5.0	1.017
6.0	1.022
8.0	1.029
10.0	1.039
15.0	1.057
20.0	1.079

TABLE 2.7. *Density of aqueous solutions of polyethylene glycol (PEG 6 000) at 20°C.*

Polymer concentration, % (w/w)	d_4^{20}
2.0	1.001
5.0	1.007
8.0	1.012
10.0	1.015
15.0	1.024
20.0	1.033
25.0	1.043

TABLE 2.8. *Density of aqueous solutions of methylcellulose (MC 4 000) at 20°C.*

Polymer concentration, % (w/w)	d_4^{20}
0.195	0.999
0.598	1.000
1.00	1.001
2.09	1.004

TABLE 2.9. *Density of aqueous solutions of hydroxypropyldextran (HPD 70) at 20°C.*

Polymer concentration, % (w/w)	d_4^{20}
1.0	1.001
2.0	1.004
3.0	1.007
4.0	1.010
5.0	1.013
10.0	1.029

TABLE 2.10. *Density of aqueous solutions of polyvinylalcohol (PVA 48/20) at 21°C.*

Polymer concentration, % (w/w)	d_4^{20}
1.0	1.000
2.0	1.003
3.0	1.005
4.0	1.008
5.0	1.011

Polymer concentration, % (w/w)	d_4^{20}
2.0	1.007
4.0	1.018
6.0	1.028
8.0	1.038
10.0	1.048
15.0	1.076
20.0	1.104

The Osmotic Pressure

Equilibrium between the two phases implies that the osmotic pressure of the two phases is the same. Beijerinck (5) pointed out that it should therefore be possible to compare the osmotic pressures of different polymer solutions. This possibility has also been discussed by Dobry (13) who measured, with an osmometer, the osmotic pressure of two phases in equilibrium and found, as expected, that it was the same for both (16).

It would be an extremely simple method of determining the osmotic pressure of a concentrated polymer solution to match it against another polymer solution, the osmotic pressure of which has once been determined by an independent method. From the phase diagrams of the dextran–polyethylene glycol systems we may, for example, notice that concentrated solutions of dextran have osmotic pressures independent of the molecular weight. If we compare the tie lines going through the point representing a mixture of 8 per cent (w/w) dextran and 6 per cent (w/w) polyethylene glycol of the diagrams in Figs. 2.11, 2.13, and 2.15 we see that a 10 per cent (w/w) solution of polyethylene glycol 6000 is always in equilibrium with a 19 per cent (w/w) solution of either dextran D 68, 48 or 37. This is most clearly seen in Fig. 2.54 where the different tie lines have been drawn together. The same result is obtained if tie lines are drawn through other points more removed from the critical points of the systems.

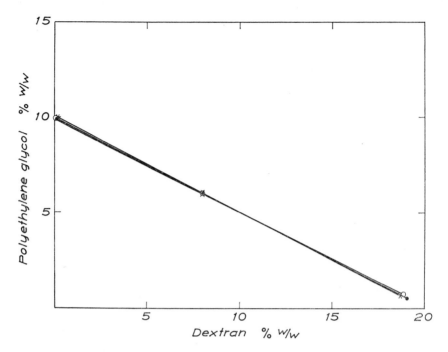

Fig. 2.54. Three tie lines connecting the two phases of three systems of dextran and polyethylene glycol with different dextran fractions. ○, D 68; ●, D 48; ×, D 37. The polyethylene glycol was PEG 6000 in all systems. Composition of the total system 8 % (w/w) dextran and 6 % polyethylene glycol at 20°C.

Influence of Low Molecular Substances on the Phase Systems

Polymer phase systems may be complemented by low molecular substances such as sucrose or salt in order to obtain a suitable environment for cell particles. The systems containing non-ionic polymers only are hardly affected by the addition of, for example, 0.1–1 molar sucrose or NaCl. Thus the critical composition of the system D 37 – PEG 6000–H_2O at 0°C is 5.2 per cent (w/w) D 37 and 3.1 per cent (w/w) PEG 6000; and the critical composition of the system D 37 – PEG 6000–10 per cent (w/w) sucrose is 5.2 per cent (w/w) dextran, 3.3 per cent (w/w) PEG 6000, and 10 per cent (w/w) sucrose. Similarly, the binodial of the system dextran–polyethylene glycol is not much changed by the addition of 0.1 M NaCl.

It is only at higher salt concentrations that an effect on the phase system may be observed. Thus, the volume ratio of the phases of the dextran–polyethylene glycol system is constant at salt concentrations up to about 0.8 M NaCl and 0.3 M phosphate buffer, pH = 7. As may be seen in Fig. 2.25, NaCl distributes almost equally between the phases of the dextran–polyethylene glycol system even at rather high salt concentrations.

Systems containing a polyelectrolyte are, however, highly dependent on the ionic composition (see below).

The Polyelectrolyte Systems — "Liquid Ion Exchangers"

Phase separation in mixtures containing a polyelectrolyte depends highly on both the ionic strength and the kind of ions present. This is most clearly shown by the systems containing dextran sulfate. Thus a mixture of Na dextran sulfate and polyethylene glycol gives a homogeneous solution if no salt is added, at least below polymer concentrations of about 20 per cent. If NaCl is added up to a concentration of 0.15 M, the mixture immediately becomes turbid and a bottom phase containing most of the dextran sulfate separates out while most of the polyethylene glycol stays in the upper phase. As the NaCl concentration is increased, the lower concentration of the polymers is needed for phase separation; see Fig. 2.33. Thus in a mixture containing 5 per cent NaDS 68 in 0.15 M NaCl at 20°, at least 8 per cent PEG 6000 is necessary for phase separation, while in the presence of 1 M NaCl only 1.5 per cent PEG 6000 is necessary for phase separation.

The concentration of polyethylene glycol which is necessary for phase separation with a certain amount of dextran sulfate depends also on the kind of salt added. The tendency to favour phase separation in a dextran sulfate–polyethylene glycol mixture thus increases with the following series of cations: $Li^+ < NH_4^+ < Na^+ < Cs^+ \leq K^+$ when these are added as chlorides. The phase separation also depends on the kind of anions; the tendency to favour phase separation decreases with the following series of anions: $NO_3^- > Cl^- > \frac{1}{2}HPO_4^{2-} > \frac{1}{2}SO_4^{2-}$ as sodium salts.

If enough salt is added polyethylene glycol may even be omitted; a system of dextran sulfate–salt–water is then obtained. Thus a two-phase system is obtained of 20 per cent dextran sulfate (NaDS 70) in

1 M NaCl in the cold. The bottom phase, which is clear and liquid, contains most of the dextran sulfate. At room temperature no phase separation is obtained even in 5 M NaCl. However, KCl precipitates dextran sulfate at concentrations above about 0.3 M at room temperature; the dextran sulfate phase is in this case turbid and highly viscous. The same consistency of the bottom phase is obtained when CsCl is used. No phase separation is obtained with dextran sulfate and LiCl or NH_4Cl, either in the cold or at room temperature. Dextran sulfate is precipitated by $BaCl_2$ but not by $CaCl_2$.

The results reported here on the phase separation in mixtures with dextran sulfate and various salts are analogous to those reported earlier by Eisenberg & Ram Mohan (18) on another sulfate polymer, namely salts of polyvinylalcoholsulfonic acid. They studied in detail the phase separation in polyvinylalcohol sulfate–salt–water mixtures and found that it depends on temperature, polymer concentration, added electrolyte concentration and the kind of ions added. Measurements of conductance and viscosity indicated a specific interaction between the polymer and the ions even at concentrations when phase separation did not occur. Qualitatively, the results obtained with dextran sulfate and polyvinylalcohol sulfate are very similar except for their behaviour in CsCl solutions: dextran sulfate is precipitated by this salt but not polyvinylalcohol sulfate.

When polyelectrolytes with other acid groups are mixed with various salts, entirely different results are obtained. Thus, the sodium salt of carboxymethyldextran does not phase separate with any of the alkali halides but it is precipitated by $BaCl_2$. In systems with polyethylene glycol and Na carboxymethyldextran the polymer concentration necessary for phase separation depends on the kind of salt present.

The Na dextran sulfate–methylcellulose system depends on the salt added in a similar manner to the Na dextran sulfate–polyethylene glycol system (see Figs. 2.35 and 2.36). Thus no phase separation occurs without the addition of salt; the same holds for the Na carboxymethyldextran–methylcellulose system. In all the systems above, one phase contains most of the polyelectrolyte. A "liquid ion exchanger" in equilibrium with a non-ionic polymer phase is thus obtained.

An interesting observation is that a mixture of Na dextran sulfate and Na carboxymethyldextran forms a phase system even without the addition of electrolytes. In this case the bottom phase contains most of the Na dextran sulfate and the top phase most of the Na carboxymethyldextran. Similar systems are Na dextran sulfate–Na carboxymethylcellulose and Na carboxymethyldextran–Na carboxymethylcellulose. In these cases we obtain two "liquid ion exchangers" in equilibrium. Although these systems are formed without the addition of salt, their phase separation still depends highly on various salts added. Phase separation is, for example, favoured at higher concentrations of salts added as is the case with the Na dextran sulfate–polyethylene glycol systems.

The results obtained on mixing solutions of Na dextran sulfate and diethylaminoethyldextran·HCl at various NaCl concentrations are particularly interesting. Thus, without, or at low concentrations of, added NaCl a more or less solid precipitate or a highly viscous bottom phase which contains both polymers is obtained. When more salt is added the mixture becomes clear. These results are to be expected from previous experimental results on phase separation between gelatin and gum arabic (7, 9, 10) when these carry opposite net charges, and also with the theory for such systems (41). The fact that the mixture becomes homogeneous when NaCl is added is thus explained as a reduction of the attractive coloumbic forces between the two oppositely charged macromolecules.

However, in the case of Na dextran sulfate–diethylaminoethyldextran·HCl when the addition of NaCl is increased, the mixture becomes turbid again, two phases are formed, and the two polymers go to different phases. Thus two "liquid ion exchangers" in equilibrium, one cationic and one anionic, are formed. This phase separation which occurs at high NaCl concentrations is probably partly due to the presence of the diethylaminoethyl groups on the one polymer. At high salt concentrations, when the attraction between the two oppositely charged macromolecules is considerably depressed, the presence of the non-polar ethyl groups on the diethylaminoethyldextran becomes of more importance and favours the "incompatibility" of the two polymers. The fact that the solubility of dextran sulfate is reduced at high salt concentrations may also favour this phase separation.

Apparently polyelectrolytes allow the construction of a large

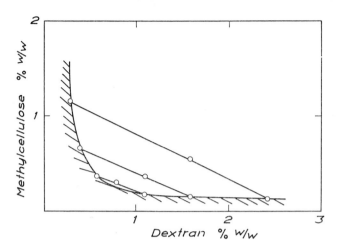

Fig. 2.55. Influence of polydispersity of the polymers in the dextran–methylcellulose system D 68–MC 4000 at 20°C. The binodial of this diagram is drawn through the experimental points (○) representing the composition of the phases. The striated area represents a region where a turbid mixture is obtained (see text).

number of liquid phase systems with highly diversified properties, which in turn increases the freedom of choosing a suitable phase system for fractionation purposes. It must be stressed, however, that polyelectrolytes usually interact more strongly with biological materials than non-ionic polymers. Thus there is a greater chance of obtaining irreversible complex formation between a protein or a cell particle and the polymer when a polyelectrolyte is used instead of a non-ionic polymer. In general, though, these interactions should be depressed at high salt concentrations.

Influence of the Polydispersity of the Polymers

As mentioned before, the fact that the polymers are polydisperse means that there is not always a sharp change from a one-phase system to a two-phase system such as indicated by a binodial. Fig. 2.55 shows the phase diagram of the system dextran–methylcellulose. The curve represents the binodial as it is obtained by drawing a line through the points representing the phase compositions. The shaded areas indicate regions where the mixtures are more or less turbid although they are represented by points outside the binodial. As

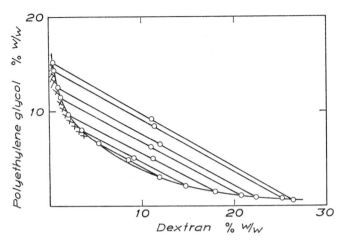

Fig. 2.56. The same as Fig. 52 for the dextran polyethylene glycol system D 17–
PEG 6 000.

may be seen in Fig. 2.55, the shaded regions are broader near the
coordinate axes but absent near the critical point. Thus, there is also
near the critical point a sharp change from a one-phase system to a
two-phase system in systems with polydisperse polymers. This is to be
expected, since at the critical composition when the two phases
theoretically become equal, no polymer fractionation takes place.
Fig. 2.56 shows the system dextran–polyethylene glycol. In this case
the polymers are not so polydisperse as in the dextran–methylcellulose
system depicted in Fig. 2.55. Therefore the shaded region is almost
absent except in the range when dextran has a low concentration.
This phase system may therefore, practically, be regarded as a ternary
system.

In general the polydispersity of the polymers is of no great practical
importance. In some cases it may even be of an advantage, namely,
for systems which are used for the concentration of virus particles
(see Chapter 7).

REFERENCES

1. ADAM, N. K., Physics and Chemistry of Surfaces, Oxford, 1941.
2. ALBERTSSON, P. Å., *Biochim. et Biophys. Acta*, *27*, 378 (1958).
3. BAKER, P. J., "Dextrans" *in* WHISTLER, R. L., and MᴇMILLER, J. N., Industrial Gums, Polysaccharides and their Derivatives, Academic Press, New York and London, 1959.
4. BEIJERINCK, M. W., *Zbl. Bakt.*, *2*, 627, 698 (1896).
5. BEIJERINCK, M. W., *Kolloid-Z.*, *7*, 16 (1910).
6. BIKERMAN, J. J., Surface Chemistry, Academic Press Inc., New York, 1958.
7. BOOIJ, H. L., and BUNGENBERG DE JONG, H. G., *in* Protoplasmatologia, edited by HEILBRUNN, L. V., and WEBER, F., Vol. 1: 2, Springer-Verlag, Vienna, 1956.
8. BRODA, A., and CHADKOWSKA, M. B., *J. Polymer Sci.*, *30*, 639 (1958).
9. BUNGENBERG DE JONG, H. G., La Coacervation, Les Coacervats et leur importance en Biologie, Tome I et II, *in Actualités sci. et ind. 397*, 1 and *398*, 1 (1936).
10. — *in* KRUYT, H. R., Colloid Science, Vol. II, Elsevier Publishing Co., Amsterdam, 1949.
11. "Carbowax Polyethylene Glycols", Carbide and Carbon Chemicals Company, New York. Copyright 1952.
12. Dervichian, D. G., *Research, London*, *2*, 210 (1949).
13. DOBRY, A., and BOYER-KAWENOKI, F., *J. Polymer Sci.*, *2*, 90, (1947).
14. DOBRY, A., *Bull. soc. chim. Belg.*, *57*, 280 (1948).
15. — *J. chim. phys.*, *35*, 387 (1938).
16. — *J. chim. phys.*, *36*, 102 (1939).
17. EINSTEIN, A., *Ann. Physik*, *19*, 289 (1909).
18. EISENBERG, H., and RAM MOHAN, G., *J. Phys. Chem.*, *63*, 671 (1959).
19. FLORY, P. J., Principles of Polymer Chemistry, Cornell University Press, Ithaca, New York, 1953.
20. GRANATH, K. A., *J. Colloid Sci.*, *13*, 308 (1958).
21. GRANATH, K. A., personal communication.
22. GREMINGER, G. K., and SAVAGE, A. B., Methylcellulose and Its Derivatives, Chapter 24 in ref. 62.
23. GRÖNWALL, A., Dextran and Its Use, *in* Colloidal Infusion Solutions. Almqvist & Wiksell, Stockholm; Academic Press Inc., New York; Blackwell Scientific Publications, Oxford, 1957.
24. HUGGINS, M. L., Physical Chemistry of High Polymers, John Wiley & Sons, Inc., New York, 1958.
25. JULLANDER, I., *Ind. Eng. Chem.*, *49*, 364 (1957).
26. — Chapter 26 in ref. 62.
27. KERN, R. J., and SLOCOMBE, R. J., *J. Polymer Sci.*, *15*, 183 (1955).
28. KERN, R. J., *J. Polymer Sci.*, *21*, 19 (1956).
29. — *J. Polymer Sci.*, *33*, 524 (1958).
30. MANLEY, R. ST. J., *Arkiv Kemi*, *9*, 519 (1956).

31. McClendon, J. H., *Plant Physiol.*, *29*, 448 (1954).
32. "Methocel", Dow Chemical Co., Midland, Mich., U.S.A. Copyright 1949.
33. Michaeli, I., Overbeek, J. Th. G., and Voorn, M. J., *J. Polymer Sci.*, *23*, 443 (1957).
34. Mora, P. T., and Wood, J. W., *J. Am. Chem. Soc.*, *80*, 685, 3700 (1958).
35. McKernan, W. M., and Ricketts, C. R., *Biochem. J.*, *76*, 117 (1960).
36. Nakajima, A., Ogawa, A., and Sakurada, I., Polymer (Japan) *14*, 596 (1957).
37. Oparin, A. I., The Origin of Life on the Earth, Chapter 7, Oliver & Boyd, Edinburgh and London, 1957.
38. Ostwald, W., and Hertel, R. H., *Kolloid-Z.*, *47*, 258 (1929).
39. — *Kolloid-Z.*, *47*, 357 (1929).
40. Ostwald, W., and Köhler, R., *Kolloid-Z.*, *43*, 131 (1927).
41. Overbeek, J. Th. G., and Voorn, M. J., *J. Cellular Comp. Physiol.*, *49*, Suppl. 1, 7 (1958).
42. Pauli, W., and Rona, F., *Hofmeisters Beitr.*, *2*, 1 (1902).
43. — *Hofmeisters Beitr.*, *3*, 225 (1903).
44. Pauli W., and Ripper, E., *Kolloid-Z.*, *62*, 162 (1933).
45. Reinders, *Chem. Weekblad*, *10* (1913).
46. Reppe, W., Polyvinylpyrrolidon, Verlag Chemie, GMBH, Weinheim/ Bergstr., Germany, 1955.
47. Ruiter, L. de, and Bungenberg de Jong, H. G., *Proc. Koninkl. Nederland. Akad. Wetenschap.*, *50*, 836 (1947).
48. Scott, R. L., *J. Chem. Phys.*, *17*, 279 (1949).
49. Silberberg, A., Interfacial Tension and Phase Separation in Two Polymer-Solvent Systems. Diss. Basel, 1952.
50. Silberberg, A., and Kuhn, W., *J. Polymer Sci.*, *13*, 21 (1954).
51. Sloan, J. W., Alexander, B. H., Lohmar, R. L., Wolff, I. A., and Rist, C. E., *J. Am. Chem. Soc.*, *76*, 4429 (1954).
52. Spiro, K., *Hofmeisters Beitr.*, *4*, 300 (1904).
53. Squire, J. R., Bull, J. P., Maycock, W. d'A., and Ricketts, C. R., Dextran, Its Properties and Use in Medicine, Blackwell Scientific Publications, Oxford, 1955.
54. Stuart, H. A., Die Physik der Hochpolymeren, Vol. 2, Springer-Verlag, Berlin, Göttingen, Heidelberg, 1953.
55. Thiele, H., and Langmaack, L., *Z. physik. Chem.*, *206*, 394 (1956).
56. Tiebackx, F. W., *Kolloid.-Z.*, *8*, 198 (1911).
57. — *ibid.*, 238 (1911).
58. Tompa, H., *Trans. Faraday Soc.*, *45*, 1142 (1949).
59. — *ibid.*, *46*, 970 (1950).
60. — Polymer Solutions, Butterworths Scientific Publications, London, 1956.
61. Treybal, R. E., Liquid Extraction, McGraw-Hill Book Company, Inc., New York, Toronto, London, 1951.
62. Whistler, R. L., and BeMiller, J. N., Industrial Gums Polysaccharides and Their Derivatives, Academic Press, New York and London, 1959.

63. Voorn, M. J., *Rec. trav. chim. Pays-Bas*, *75*, 317 (1956).

64. — *ibid.*, *75*, 405 (1956).

65. — *ibid.*, *75*, 427 (1956).

66. — *ibid.*, 75, 925 (1956).

67. — *ibid.*, *75*, 1021 (1956).

68. — Fortschritte der Hochpolymeren-Forschung, *Advances in Polymer   Sci.*, *1*, 192 (1959).

69. Zernike, J., Chemical Phase Theory, N. V. Uitgevers-Maatschappij Æ. E. Kluwer, Deventer, Antwerp, Djakarta, 1955.

3. The Distribution of Particles in a Two-Phase System—Theory

THE DISTRIBUTION OF PARTICLES DUE TO BROWNIAN MOTION AND THE INTERFACIAL FORCES

Two tendencies oppose each other in determining the distribution of particles in a two-phase system. One is the thermal motion of the particles—the so-called Brownian motion—which tends to distribute the particles randomly throughout the entire space of the phase system. The other is the forces acting upon the particles at the interface tending to distribute them unevenly so that they collect in the phase in which they have their lowest energy. If the work needed to move a particle from phase 1 to phase 2 against these forces is ΔE, then according to the theory of Brownian motion (6, 7) the following relation should hold:

$$\frac{C_2}{C_1} = e^{-\frac{\Delta E}{kT}} \tag{1}$$

where C_1 and C_2 are the concentrations of particles in phases 1 and 2 respectively, k is the Boltzmann constant and T is the temperature.

In the following, ΔE is calculated for a spherical particle of radius R assumed to have a perfectly uniform interface separating it from the surrounding medium and gravitational forces are neglected. Interfaces are characterized by possessing a certain amount of free surface energy per unit surface area. This is called the interfacial tension and may be expressed in ergs/cm²; an interface with an interfacial tension γ ergs/cm² and an area of A cm² therefore has a free energy of $A\gamma$ ergs. This energy is "stored" in the interface, it has to be supplied when the interface is formed and is released when the interface disappears. The interfacial free energy of the particle in a liquid two-phase system can be considered as a function of the position of the particle in the phase system (see Fig. 3.1). There are three different kinds of interfaces:

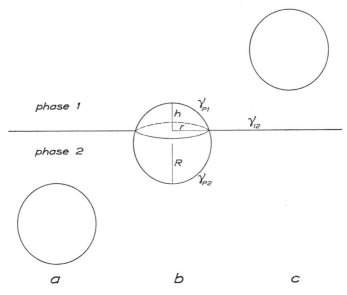

Fig. 3.1. A spherical particle at three different positions in a liquid two-phase system. γ_{12} is the interfacial tension between the two phases; γ_{P1} between the particle and phase 1; and γ_{P2} between the particle and phase 2.

(1) The liquid–liquid interface between the two phases of the system. Let this interfacial tension be γ_{12} ergs/cm².

(2) The particle–liquid interface between the particle and the top phase. Let this interfacial tension be γ_{P1} ergs/cm².

(3) The particle–liquid interface between the particle and the bottom phase. Let this interfacial tension be γ_{P2} ergs/cm².

When the particle is entirely in the lower phase, as at position a in Fig. 3.1, its interfacial free energy, G^s is

$$G_2^s = 4\pi R^2 \gamma_{P2}. \tag{2}$$

Let us suppose that the particle is shifted perpendicularly upwards. When the particle has moved through the distance h partly into the top phase, as at position b in Fig. 3.1, then a new interface between the particle and the top phase of area $2\pi Rh$ has been formed. This increases the free surface energy of the particle by $2\pi Rh\gamma_{P1}$ ergs. Simultaneously, the area of the interface between the particle and the bottom phase has decreased by the same extent resulting in a loss of $2\pi Rh\gamma_{P2}$ ergs in free surface energy of the particle. In addition, an area of πr^2 of the liquid–liquid interface between the top phase and the bottom phase has disappeared (r is the radius of the circle of contact between the particle and the liquid–liquid interface). Hence there is a further decrease in free surface energy of $\pi r^2 \gamma_{12}$ ergs. The potential energy of the particle caused by interfacial forces at position b, will therefore be

$$G_h^s = 4\pi R^2 \gamma_{P2} + 2\pi R h \gamma_{P1} - 2\pi R h \gamma_{P2} - \pi r^2 \gamma_{12} \tag{3}$$

but
$$r^2 = h(2R - h)$$

hence
$$G_h^s = \pi [2 R h (\gamma_{P1} - \gamma_{P2} - \gamma_{12}) + h^2 \gamma_{12}] + 4\pi R^2 \gamma_{P2}. \tag{4}$$

When h exceeds $2R$, as at position c in Fig. 3.1, that is when the particle is entirely in the top phase, the interfacial free energy of the particle is
$$G_1^s = 4\pi R^2 \gamma_{P1}. \tag{5}$$

Differentiation of eqn. (4) gives

$$\frac{d G^s}{d h} = \pi [2 R (\gamma_{P1} - \gamma_{P2} - \gamma_{12}) + 2 h \gamma_{12}] \tag{6}$$

$$\frac{d^2 G^s}{d h^2} = 2\pi \gamma_{12}. \tag{7}$$

Analysis of eqns. (6) and (7) shows that G_s will have a minimum at the following h value:

$$h_{\min} = R \left(1 - \frac{\gamma_{P1} - \gamma_{P2}}{\gamma_{12}} \right). \tag{8}$$

Since $0 < h_{\min} < 2R$ it follows that this minimum value of G^s only occurs when the value of the term on the right hand side of eqn. (8) lies between 0 and $2R$. G^s will therefore only have a minimum value when the following condition is fulfilled:

$$\left| \frac{\gamma_{P1} - \gamma_{P2}}{\gamma_{12}} \right| < 1. \tag{9}$$

The particle will then lie at its most stable position at the interface. However, if the following relation holds

$$\left| \frac{\gamma_{P1} - \gamma_{P2}}{\gamma_{12}} \right| \geqq 1 \tag{10}$$

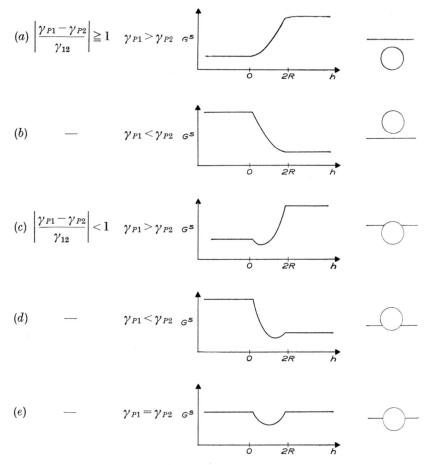

Fig. 3.2. The potential energy, G^s, of a spherical particle as a function of h (see Fig. 3.1) at different mutual relations between γ_{12}, γ_{P1} and γ_{P2}. When $h < 0$ the particle is entirely in the bottom phase; when $0 < h < 2R$ the particle passes through the interface; and when $h > 2R$ the particle is entirely in the top phase. All the curved lines are paraboloid. To the right, the G^s minimum position of the particle is shown.

then G^s will have no minimum and the particle will have its most stable position in one of the phases. These two latter relations were first deduced by Des Coudres (3).

Further analysis of eqn. (4) shows that the graph relating G^s to h will have different shapes depending on the relative values of the different surface tensions. The five main cases are shown in Fig. 3.2. In the first and second cases (Figs. 3.2a and b) the relation (10) is assumed to hold and G^s has no minimum for a unique value of h

between $h=0$ and $h=2R$. If $\gamma_{P1} > \gamma_{P2}$ (Fig. 3.2a), the particle will have its lowest energy in the bottom phase. The free surface energy difference resulting when the particle is moved from phase 2 to phase 1 is obtained by subtracting eqn. (2) from (5) and is

$$G_1^s - G_2^s = 4\pi R^2 (\gamma_{P1} - \gamma_{P2}). \tag{11}$$

Similarly, if $\gamma_{P1} < \gamma_{P2}$ (Fig. 3.2b) the particle will have its lowest energy in the top phase. The free surface energy difference between the two phases is then obtained by subtracting eqn. (5) from (2) and is

$$G_2^s - G_1^s = 4\pi R^2 (\gamma_{P2} - \gamma_{P1}). \tag{12}$$

In the remaining cases (Figs. 3.2c, d, and e), condition (9) is assumed to be fulfilled and the particle will have its lowest energy at the interface. Depending on whether γ_{P1} is larger, smaller, or equal to γ_{P2} the three cases c, d, and e respectively are obtained. The energy difference of the particle between the two phases will be that expressed by eqns. (11) and (12). The energy difference of the particle between the top phase and the G^s minimum position at the interface is obtained by substituting the h_{min} value of eqn. (8) into eqn. (4) and subtracting (4) from (5) yielding

$$G_1^s - G_{min}^s = \frac{\pi R^2 (\gamma_{P2} - \gamma_{P1} - \gamma_{12})^2}{\gamma_{12}}. \tag{13}$$

Similarly the energy difference between the bottom phase and the G^s minimum position at the interface is

$$G_2^s - G_{min}^s = \frac{\pi R^2 (\gamma_{P1} - \gamma_{P2} - \gamma_{12})^2}{\gamma_{12}}. \tag{14}$$

When $\gamma_{P1} = \gamma_{P2}$ (Fig. 3c), the energy difference between the top (or the bottom phase) and the G^s minimum position at the interface is

$$G_{1 \text{ or } 2}^s - G_{min}^s = \pi R^2 \gamma_{12}. \tag{15}$$

The distribution of a number of similar particles between the two phases is now obtained by substituting the difference in energy of one particle, as calculated above, into equation (1). Thus in the case of Fig. 3.2 a the distribution will be:

$$\frac{C_1}{C_2} = K = e^{\frac{-4\pi R^2 (\gamma_{P1} - \gamma_{P2})}{kT}}, \tag{16}$$

where K is the partition coefficient; more generally if a particle is not spherical:

$$K = e^{\frac{-A(\gamma_{P_1} - \gamma_{P_2})}{kT}},\tag{17}$$

where A is the surface area. From this important equation we may infer that the partition coefficient in a given phase system is highly dependent both on the surface area of the particle and its surface properties. For particles with identical surface properties but with different surface areas the partition coefficient depends only on the surface area, $\gamma_{P1} - \gamma_{P2}$ being a constant; and

$$K = e^{\frac{A\lambda}{kT}},\tag{18}$$

where $\lambda = -(\gamma_{P1} - \gamma_{P2})$. This is of a similar form as the expression derived by Brønsted (1, 2) and mentioned in Chapter 1

$$K = e^{\frac{M\lambda}{kT}}\tag{19}$$

(where M = molecular weight). It was deduced for so-called iso-chemical substances, that is substances which differ in molecular weight only. As pointed out by Brønsted, M should be replaced by the surface area for large and more or less spherical molecules (1).

As may be seen from equation (17), the partition coefficient tends to become larger $(\gamma_{P1} < \gamma_{P2})$ or smaller $(\gamma_{P1} > \gamma_{P2})$ as the surface area of the particles increases. A more unilateral distribution is therefore obtained and two kinds of particles will be more completely separated the larger their particle size, if for one species $\gamma_{P1} > \gamma_{P2}$ and for the other $\gamma_{P1} < \gamma_{P2}$. From a theoretical point of view two-phase systems therefore seem to be very suitable for the fractionation of large particle weight substances.

The distribution of the particles between one of the phases and the G^s minimum position at the interface is obtained by putting the energy difference of the particle as expressed by eqn. (13) into eqn. (1).

Thus

$$\frac{a_{\min}}{C_1} = e^{\frac{\pi R^2 (\gamma_{P2} - \gamma_{P1} - \gamma_{12})^2}{\gamma_{12} kT}}\tag{20}$$

where $a_{\min}$ is the number of particles in the G^s minimum position per cm^2 and C_1 is the number of particles per ml top phase.

100

In the special case when $\gamma_{P1}=\gamma_{P2}$ the adsorption will follow the following equation:

$$\frac{a_{\min}}{C} = e^{\frac{\pi R^2 \gamma_{12}}{kT}}, \tag{21}$$

where C is the concentration of particles in the top and bottom phases. All particles located between $h=0$ and $h=2R$ (Fig. 3.2) should be considered as adsorbed at the interface and their number per cm² (a) is obtained by summing up all particles present at different positions between $h=0$ and $h=2R$.

The following important conclusions can be drawn from eqns. (20) and (21).

(1) For different particles with similar interfacial tensions in a given phase system, that is when γ_{P1}, γ_{P2} and γ_{12} are constant, the tendency for adsorption at the interface will be greater the larger the radius of the particles.

(2) For any particle having the same partition coefficient in different phase systems (i.e. when R, γ_{P1} and γ_{P2} are constant, see eqn. (16)), the tendency for adsorption at the interface will be greater the larger the value of γ_{12}.

The special case of eqn. (21) when $\gamma_{P1}=\gamma_{P2}$ (Fig. 3.2 e) is particularly interesting, since the distribution between the phases and the interface is only determined by the radius of the particle and the liquid–liquid interfacial tension, γ_{12} of the phase system. Thus any particle, irrespective of its nature, having the same affinity for both phases of a phase system (i.e. its partition coefficient $=1$) must be more or less concentrated at the interface. This is probably one of the reasons why it is often so difficult to distribute large molecules such as proteins with a partition coefficient around unity in low molecular weight phase systems. Both the size of the protein molecules and the γ_{12} value of these systems are so large that the protein is almost entirely adsorbed at the interface when the system is such that the protein has about the same affinity for both phases. As an example, we may calculate the quotient $a_{\min}/c$ in eqn. (21) for a particle of radius 3 mμ and a phase system with an interfacial tension of 1 erg/cm² at 20°C. These values correspond in order of magnitude to a protein molecule with a molecular weight of about 100 000 and the interfacial tension of a water-butanol system. The chosen values will show that $a_{\min}/c$ is about 10³ ; for larger particles it will be even higher.

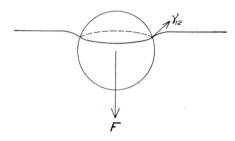

Fig. 3.3. A particle at an interface under the gravitational force F, which is counter-acted by an upward force equal to γ_{12} times the circumference of the circle of contact between the particle and the liquid–liquid interface.

An other interesting result of eqn. (21) is that it would be possible to estimate the interfacial tension of a phase system by studying the adsorption of a number of particles all having a partition coefficient of unity but differing in radius.

THE INFLUENCE OF GRAVITY

When the particle is denser than the phases, the particle is pulled down by a force F (see Fig. 3.3) which depends upon the size and density of the particle and the density of the phases. This force is counter-acted by an upward force depending on the vertical component of γ_{12} and the circumference of the circle of contact between the particle and the liquid–liquid interface. When the latter force can overcome the gravitational force the particle remains at the interface. Equations that describe the relationship fulfilling this condition have been deduced for particles of different shapes in connection with flotation studies; see for example the books of Gaudin (8) and Taggart (12).

We shall now consider the magnitude of the forces involved. Suppose that a spherical particle of radius one micron and a density of 1.3 is attached at the interface of a system having an interfacial tension of 0.001 dyne/cm and that the circle of contact between the particle and the interface equals the diameter of the particle. For simplicity, the densities of the phases are considered to be unity. The gravitational force F acting downwards on the particle will then be

$$F = g \cdot \tfrac{4}{3}\pi \cdot 10^{-12} \cdot 0.3 \text{ dynes,}$$

where $g \, (= 981 \text{ cm/sec}^2)$ is the gravitational constant. The upward force on the particle is

$$0.001 \cdot 2 \cdot \pi \cdot 10^{-4} \text{ dynes.}$$

F will be of the order of 10^{-9} dynes while the upward force will be of the order of 10^{-6} dynes.

For smaller particles the interfacial force will be still larger compared with the gravitational force and we may therefore conclude, that for the kind of particles studied here, gravitation has in most cases only a small influence on the distribution of a single particle. If, however, an interface becomes overloaded with particles, so that several layers of particles are collected on it, then clumps of particles may fall from the interface due to gravitation.

THE INFLUENCE OF SHAKING

Theoretically, equilibrium may be obtained by adding the particles to a phase system and then allowing them to distribute by their own thermal motion. In practice this would take too long since the diffusion of the particles is very slow. To achieve equilibrium quickly one shakes the phase system containing the particles, so that a close contact between the two phases and the particles is obtained within a short time. During the shaking the particles may be subjected to various mechanical forces, for example centrifugal and frictional forces supplying the particles with kinetic energy in addition to that of the thermal motion. These effects are probably proportionally much greater for large particles such as whole cells.

It should also be pointed out that, while the distribution of the particles takes place during shaking, the experimental determination of the particle distribution is done after the two phases have separated and formed the final horizontal interface. The partition coefficient of a substance has probably the same value during shaking and after separation. However, the magnitude of adsorption at the large "interface" formed during shaking may be different from that occurring at the final horizontal interface. At present there seems to be no method available for determining the total interfacial area (and hence the value of a in eqns. (20) and (21)) formed during shaking.

Nevertheless as a rough guide we may use eqns. (20) and (21) if we wish to study the factors determining the adsorption at the final horizontal interface when condition (9) is fulfilled.

THE RELATION BETWEEN THE PARTITION
COEFFICIENT AND THE ACTIVITY

When two phases are in equilibrium the chemical potential of the ith component is the same in both phases.

$$\mu_{i,1} = \mu_{i,2}, \tag{22}$$

where 1 and 2 denote the top and bottom phases respectively. Choosing the same standard state μ_i^0 for both phases we may write

$$\mu_i^0 + RT \ln f_{i,1} C_{i,1} = \mu_i^0 + RT \ln f_{i,2} C_{i,2}, \tag{23}$$

where C is the molar concentration and f is the activity coefficient. Thus

$$\frac{C_{i,1}}{C_{i,2}} = \frac{f_{i,2}}{f_{i,1}} = K, \tag{24}$$

where K is the partition coefficient. With the standard state chosen here the partition coefficient is thus inversely proportional to the ratio between the activity coefficients of the substance in the top and bottom phases.

THE DONNAN EFFECT

When partitioned macromolecules or particles carry a net electrical charge and they distribute in a manner different from other ions, this can create an electrical potential between the phases. This is the well known Donnan effect (4, 9, 10). Thus, for example, the Donnan effect plays a part when a solution of charged macromolecules is separated from a salt solution by a membrane permeable to the small ions but not to the macromolecules. The Donnan effect has thus to be considered in measurements of the osmotic pressure of proteins. (5). It also enters in ultracentrifugation (11, 13) where charged macromolecules and small ions move with different velocities.

The condition for equilibrium between two phases involving charged molecules is that the so-called electrochemical potential (φ) of the ith component is the same in both phases.

This potential may be written as

$$\varphi_i = \mu_i + Fz V, \tag{25}$$

where F is the Faraday constant, z the net electronic charge of the molecules and V the electrical potential of the phase. Thus, at equilibrium

$$\mu_i^0 + RT \ln f_{i,1} C_{i,1} + F z_i V_1 = \mu_i^0 + RT \ln f_{i,2} C_{i,2} + F z_i V_2. \qquad (26)$$

By solving eqn. (26) we obtain

$$\ln K_i^* = \ln \frac{C_{i,1}}{C_{i,2}} = \ln \frac{f_{i,2}}{f_{i,1}} + \frac{F z_i (V_2 - V_1)}{RT} \qquad (27)$$

or

$$\ln K_i^* = \ln K_i + \frac{F z_i (V_2 - V_1)}{RT}, \qquad (28)$$

where K is the partition coefficient in the absence and K^* the partition coefficient in the presence of an electrical potential difference.

Let us now consider the partition of a protein in a two-phase system at a pH on the basic side of the isoelectric point of the protein. We may denote the protein molecule $\mathrm{Na}_z \cdot \mathrm{P}$ and assume that it dissociates into $z\mathrm{Na}^+$ ions and the P^{z-} ion. In addition Na^+ and Cl^- ions are also present in the phase system. Electroneutrality in the two phases requires that

$$C_{\mathrm{Na}^+,1} = C_{\mathrm{Cl}^-,1} + z\, C_{\mathrm{P}^{z-},1} \qquad (29)$$

and

$$C_{\mathrm{Na}^+,2} = C_{\mathrm{Cl}^-,2} + z\, C_{\mathrm{P}^{z-},2}. \qquad (30)$$

We may further assume that the activity coefficients of Na^+ and Cl^- ions are the same in both phases. This is usually the case for electrolytes in aqueous polymer–polymer two-phase systems in which electrolytes partition with a K value very near to unity i.e. $f_{i,2}/f_{i,1} = 1$ according to eqn. (24). Hence eqn. (27) for the Na^+ and Cl^- ions becomes

$$\ln \frac{C_{\mathrm{Na}^+,1}}{C_{\mathrm{Na}^+,2}} = \frac{F(V_2 - V_1)}{RT}, \qquad (31)$$

$$\ln \frac{C_{\mathrm{Cl}^-,1}}{C_{\mathrm{Cl}^-,2}} = -\frac{F(V_2 - V_1)}{RT}. \qquad (32)$$

Substituting eqn. (31) in (28) gives for K^* value of the protein

$$\ln K_{\mathrm{P}}^* = \ln K_{\mathrm{P}} - z \ln \frac{C_{\mathrm{Na}^+,1}}{C_{\mathrm{Na}^+,2}}. \qquad (33)$$

We now consider two cases in which the protein concentration is

(1) large, and (2) small compared to the equivalent Cl^- concentration.

1. $z C_{P^z-} \gg C_{Cl^-}$; this gives

$$C_{Na^+,1} = z C_{P^z-,1} \qquad (34)$$

$$C_{Na^+,2} = z C_{P^z-,2} \qquad (35)$$

and by putting these values in eqn. (33) and noting that

$$\frac{C_{P^z-,1}}{C_{P^z-,2}} = K^*$$

we obtain $\quad \ln K_P^* = \ln K_P - z \ln K_P^* \quad$ or $\quad \ln K_P^* = \dfrac{\ln K_P}{z+1}$.

As a result the numerical value of $\ln K^*$ is reduced, or the K^* value approaches unity, the larger the charge on the protein. The Donnan effect thus tends to distribute a charged molecule or particle more equally between the two phases.

2. $z C_{P^z-} \ll C_{Cl^-}$. In this case

$$C_{Na^+,1} = C_{Cl^-,1}$$

$$C_{Na^+,2} = C_{Cl^-,2}$$

and substituting these in eqns. (31) and (32) and then subtracting (32) from (31) we obtain $V_2 = V_1$. Thus in an excess of a salt such as NaCl which distributes equally between the phases, the potential difference between the two phases may be neglected and the K value of the protein obtained.

In order to test if Donnan effects are present one may, theoretically, therefore study the partition coefficient as a function of protein concentration at a constant salt concentration provided the increase in protein concentration does not change its activity coefficients. If Donnan effects are present, the partition coefficient should change from a value, K, towards another value, K^*, closer to unity as the protein concentration is increased.

The addition of salt in excess of the equivalent protein concentration to reduce the Donnan effect, is also used in measurements of the osmotic pressure for molecular weight determinations and in studies on the sedimentation of charged macromolecules.

SUMMARY

The theoretical considerations of this chapter may be summarized as follows.

If a suspension of particles with identical properties are shaken in a liquid-liquid two-phase system, their tendency to collect in one of the phases will be greater the larger the particle size, provided there is no adsorption (relation (10)) at the interface.

If the same particles are shaken in a system where the conditions for adsorption at the interface (relation (9)) are fulfilled, then the attachment of the particles to the interface will be more favoured the larger their size and the larger the interfacial tension of the system.

These phenomena will be discussed in Chapter 4 in relation to experimental results.

REFERENCES

1. BRØNSTED, J. N., *Z. phys. Chem.*, *A* (Bodenstein-Festband), p. 257 (1931).
2. BRØNSTED, J. N., and WARMING, E., *Z. phys. Chem.*, *A 155*, 343 (1931).
3. DES COUDRES, T., *in* RHUMBLER, L., *Wilhelm Roux' Arch. Entwicklungs-mech. Organ.*, *7*, 225 (1898).
4. DONNAN, F. G., *Z. Elektrochem.*, *17*, 572 (1911).
5. EDSALL, J. T., *in* NEURATH, H., and BAILEY, K., The Proteins, Vol. 1, part B, Academic Press Inc., New York, 1953.
6. EINSTEIN, A., *Ann. Physik*, *19*, 371 (1906).
7. — Investigations on the Theory of the Brownian Movement, Dover Publications, Inc. New York, 1956.
8. GAUDIN, A. M., Flotation, McGraw-Hill Book Co., Inc., New York, 1957.
9. OVERBEEK, J. TH. G., *Progr. in Biophysics and Biophys. Chem.*, *6*, 57 (1956).
10. — *in* Colloid Science, edited by H. R. KRUYT, Vol. 1, p. 188, Elsevier Publishing Company, Amsterdam, 1952.
11. SVEDBERG, T., and PEDERSEN, K. O., The Ultracentrifuge, Clarendon Press, Oxford, 1940.
12. TAGGART, A. F., Elements of Ore Dressing, p. 246, John Wiley & Sons, Inc., New York, 1951.
13. TISELIUS, A., *Kolloid-Z.*, *59*, 306 (1932).

4. The Distribution of Particles and Macromolecules in Polymer Two-Phase Systems—Experimental

INTRODUCTION

The experiments described in this chapter have been carried out in order to study some of the more important factors determining the behaviour of particles and macromolecules in a polymer two-phase system. It would be expected that the distribution is determined, for example, by the nature and the size of the particle surface, the constitution of the polymer molecules including the number of polar and non polar groups, the molecular size and structure, and the ionic composition and pH of the phase system.

Considering the great variation in the properties of macromolecules and particles of biochemical origin, the distribution will almost certainly be a complex phenomenon, difficult to predict or interpret. In addition, we must consider the fundamental difficulty of surface chemistry, namely that even if the chemical composition of a particle as a whole is known, our knowledge regarding the composition of its surface layer is rather deficient.

Nonetheless it has been possible to study some of the factors mentioned above, more or less independently of the others and in this way a certain regularity in the behaviour of the particles has been found.

The experimental work will be described in the following sections:

(*1*) The substances and techniques used for the distribution experiments,

(*2*) The influence of the composition of the phase system in relation to its critical point,

(*3*) The influence of the molecular weights of the polymers,

(*4–7*) The distribution of a number of particles and macromolecules such as whole cells, virus particles, proteins, and nucleic acids, which is described for each phase system separately.

1. MATERIALS AND TECHNIQUES

The preparation and properties of the following substances have been described elsewhere: starch grains (2), cellulose particles (2), polystyrene latex particles (2), *Chlorella* (2), proteins (4, 5), phages (4), and viruses (24, 31).

Preliminary Experiments with Particles

The particles studied have generally had a higher density than either of the two liquid phases. The sedimentation of the particles is, except in systems very near the critical point, negligibly small compared with the time required for phase separation. In preliminary experiments the particles may be shaken with the phase system in a test tube and after the two phases have separated, the location of the particles can be determined by visual inspection of the colour or turbidity of the phases. Since emulsification is sometimes considerable this phenomenon must be taken into account in ascertaining which phase contains the particles. For example, particles present at the interface are attached to the small drops forming the emulsion, and these droplets loaded with particles may remain suspended in one phase long after the main bulk of the phases has separated. This may result in the misleading impression that the particles are freely suspended in the phase. Such an error can be eliminated by varying the volumes of the phases. As mentioned in Chapter 2, the formation of an emulsion depends upon the relative volumes of the two phases, so that it is usually a part of the smaller phase which remains in droplet form within the other phase (Fig. 2.53). Thus, if the particles are shaken in one test tube with a small bottom phase and a large top phase, and in another test tube with a large bottom phase and a small top phase, it is usually possible to detect whether or not the particles are freely suspended in a phase. It may also sometimes be useful to check this by microscopical examination.

Determination of the Partition Coefficient

For quantitative experiments on a 10–20 ml scale the distribution is made in a separating funnel of the form shown in Fig. 4.1. A cork is used for closing the funnel because a glass stopper sometimes sticks when the polymer solutions dry between the ground surfaces; the cork may be covered with an aluminium foil to prevent contamination by any impurity or dust from the cork. The tube below the outlet should be at least 0.5 cm in diameter. The phases are mixed by inverting the funnel several times (not by vigorous agitation). After the phases have again separated, samples from the top phase are removed by pipette and samples from the bottom phase through the funnel outlet.

When smaller volumes (0.5–2 ml) of the phases are used, it is more convenient to perform the distribution in a small test tube. Samples are withdrawn from the lower part of the bottom phase using a pipette; sometimes it may be convenient to use a plastic test tube in which a small hole can be made.

Determination of the Adsorption of Particles at the Interface

Both direct and indirect methods have been used for the determination of particles attached to the interface (2).

When there is a distribution of particles between the bottom phase and the interface, the direct method is as follows. After the two phases have separated, and a horizontal interface has formed, the free particles in the bottom phase are allowed to sediment to the bottom of the tube, while those attached to the interface are carefully withdrawn with a pipette placed just above the interface. This method obviously works only when the particles are denser than the bottom phase, and conversely, in the case of distribution of the particles between the top phase and the interface, when the particles are less dense than the top phase.

The indirect method is as follows. Samples from the top and bottom phases are taken immediately after phase separation. The concentration of the particles in these samples is determined, and if the volumes of the phases are known, the amount of particles present in both phases may be calculated. This value is then subtracted from the total amount of particles to yield the amount adsorbed at the interface.

A very simple though less accurate method of estimating the relative amount of substance collected at the interface, is to allow phase separation to take place in a narrow graduated tube, for example, a 0.1–1 ml graduated pipette. The surface of the phase boundary is

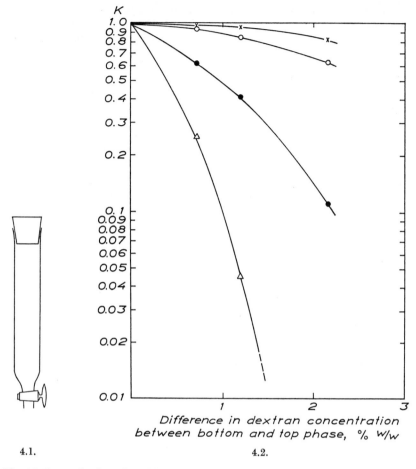

4.1.   4.2.

Fig. 4.1. Separating funnel used for quantitative determinations of partition coefficients.

Fig. 4.2. Partition coefficients, K, for CO-hemoglobin ($\times$), phycoerythrin ($\bigcirc$), hemocyanin, "one-eighth molecules" ($\bullet$), and hemocyanin, "whole molecules" ($\triangle$) in three different compositions of the dextran–methylcellulose system D68–MC4000, at 20°C. The values from Table 4.1 are plotted against the difference in dextran concentration between the two phases as obtained from the phase diagram (Fig. 2.26).

then small and the attached substance collects as a zone with a certain depth and whose volume increases approximately proportionally to the amount of substance collected at the interface. However, the zone is not always stable and material sediments. This method has been used for recording the amount of antigen–antibody precipitate formed in a two-phase system (see Fig. 8.4).

111

Stock Mixtures of Polymer Solutions

It is convenient to use a stock mixture of the polymer solutions. To a sample of this stock mixture a certain volume of the particle suspension, and if necessary a given volume of a salt solution, is added to complete the final phase system. In studying, for example, the distribution of a suspension of cells in 10 g of a phase system containing 5 per cent (w/w) D 68 and 4 per cent (w/w) PEG 6000 in the presence of 0.01 M NaCl, the following procedure may be used. A stock mixture is first prepared by mixing 25 g of a 20 per cent (w/w) solution of D 68, 20 g of a 20 per cent (w/w) solution of PEG 6000, and 35 g water. On dilution of this mixture from 8 g to 10 g, a mixture with the desired concentrations of the polymers is obtained. The stock mixture is therefore shaken and then immediately, before separation of the phases occurs, a sample is withdrawn using a pipette with a wide orifice and 8 g are transferred to a tube containing 1 g of the cell suspension and 1 ml of 0.1 M NaCl on an automatic recording balance, (for example Mettler, type K7).

It should be noted that the salt concentrations are not completely defined since the concentrations in the two phases may be slightly different and thus each differs from the mean concentration in the mixture.

2. THE DISTRIBUTION IN SYSTEMS WITH COMPOSITIONS MORE OR LESS REMOVED FROM THE CRITICAL POINT

Brønsted (11, 12) studied the distribution of colloidal arsenic sulfide and chromous hydroxide in a two-phase system of water, butanol, and ethanol, and found that the distribution was more unilateral the further the composition was removed from the critical point. Similar results were obtained by Tavel who determined the partition coefficient of horse serum albumin and gamma globulin at different compositions near the critical point of a system of water, magnesium sulfate, and diethylcarbitol (30).

Further phenomena of this type are summarized in Table 4.1, which gives the distributions of some proteins in three different compositions of the dextran-methylcellulose system. The three systems are marked A1, B, and C in Fig. 2.26. As may be seen in Table 4.1, the partition

TABLE 4.1. *Partition coefficients of four proteins in three dextran–methylcellulose systems with different compositions. The compositions of systems A1, B, and C are given in Fig. 2.26. The data are plotted in Fig. 4.2. Temperature: 20°C.*

Protein	Partition coefficients		
	System A1	System B	System C
CO-hemoglobin	0.99	0.96	0.83
Phycoerythrin	0.95	0.85	0.63
Hemocyanin, "eighth"	0.62	0.41	0.11
Hemocyanin, "whole"	0.25	0.045	< 0.01
Difference in dextran concentration between the bottom and top phases % (w/w)	0.71	1.19	2.14

coefficient is less than 1 for all the proteins studied and is lower for the systems further from the critical composition. In all three systems, large particles like *Chlorella* cells, bacteria, and erythrocytes have partition coefficients near zero and are not adsorbed at the interface. (The distribution of such large particles nearer to the critical point than system A1 cannot be investigated since the particles sediment to the bottom of the tube before the phases have separated due to the long time required for phase separation.)

A similar experiment with serum albumin and phycoerythrin in the dextran–polyethylene glycol system is summarized in Table 4.2. In this system larger particles are often adsorbed at the interface. The results obtained when *Chlorella* cells, erythrocytes, *Echerichia coli*, tobacco mosaic virus, and *Helix pomatia* hemocyanin are distributed in dextran–polyethylene glycol systems having different compositions are shown in Table 4.3. As may be seen, the interfacial adsorption increases the further the system is removed from its critical composition. Adsorption also occurs more frequently for the larger particles. Thus proteins in the molecular weight range between 10,000 and about one million are usually not adsorbed at the interface but partition between the phases giving rise to a finite partition coefficient.

As a measure of how far a system is removed from the critical point, the difference in any physical or chemical property between the two phases can be used. Tavel (30) has, for example, characterized the

TABLE 4.2. *Partition coefficients of human serum albumin and phycoerythrin in three differerent compositions of the dextran–polyethylene glycol system, D 48 – PEG 6000 (see Fig. 2.13), and in two salt media. Temperature: 20°C. The data are plotted in Fig. 4.3.*

Protein	Partition coefficients		
	System 1 5 % (w/w) D 3.5 % (w/w) PEG	System 2 7 % (w/w) D 3 % (w/w) PEG	System 3 9 % (w/w) D 3 % (w/w) PEG
In 0.01 *M* K phosphate, pH = 6.8:			
Serum albumin	0.9	0.8	0.6
Phycoerythrin	2.0	3.4	5.6
In 0.01 *M* K phosphate, pH = 6.8, + 0.1 *M* NaCl:			
Serum albumin	0.65	0.33	0.2
Phycoerythrin	0.90	0.74	0.49
Difference in dextran conc. between bottom and top phase % (w/w)	5.54	8.5	12.7

TABLE 4.3. *Approximate amounts of particles collected at the interface in three different dextran–polyethylene glycol systems. (The polymer compositions are the same as in Table 4.2.)*

Particle	Salt	Percentage particles adsorbed at the interface		
		System 1	System 2	System 3
Erythrocytes (human)	0.1 *M* Na phosphate, pH = 6.8	0–20	80	100
Chlorella	0.01 *M* Na phosphate, pH = 6.8	0	0	0–10
E. coli	0.1 *M* Na phosphate, pH = 6.8		30	
Tobacco mosaic virus	0.01 *M* Na phosphate, pH = 6.8	0	10	20
Hemocyanin "whole"	0.01 *M* Na phosphate, pH = 6.0	10	10	40

composition of a system by measuring the difference in the density of the two phases; this may be conveniently measured using a Westphal balance and is particularly suitable for systems very close to the critical composition. For the systems described here, the difference in concentration of one of the polymers between the phases may be used as a

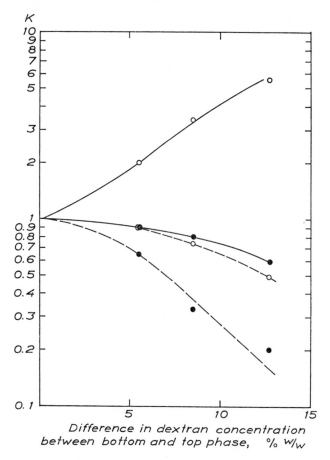

Fig. 4.3. Partition coefficients, K, for phycoerythrin ($\bigcirc$), and serum albumin ($\bullet$) in three different compositions of the dextran–polyethylene glycol system D 48–PEG 6000, at 20°C. The K values of Table 4.2 are plotted against the difference in dextran concentration between the two phases as obtained from the phase diagram (Fig. 2.13). Whole lines: in 0.01 M phosphate buffer, pH = 6.8; broken lines: in 0.01 M phosphate buffer, pH = 6.8, and 0.1 M NaCl.

measure of how far the system is removed from the critical point. Thus the K values given in Tables 4.1 and 4.2 are plotted as ordinates and the difference in dextran concentration between the phases of the different systems as abscissae in Figs. 4.2 and 4.3 respectively. This difference in dextran concentration is obtained from the phase diagrams (see Figs. 2.13 and 2.26).

3. INFLUENCE OF THE MOLECULAR WEIGHTS OF THE POLYMERS

Tables 4.4 and 4.5 show the result when different particles and proteins are distributed in the dextran–polyethylene glycol and salt–polyethylene glycol systems with different fractions of the polymers. It may be seen in the Table 4.4 that some particles, such as those of starch and cellulose, always remain in the same phase while others such as *Chlorella* or erythrocytes, either change phase or become adsorbed to the interface when the molecular weight of one polymer is changed.

Such a change, however, is always in the same direction that is the particles have more affinity for a phase if the polymer of this phase is replaced by a lower molecular weight fraction of the same polymer. No exception to this rule has yet been found among a great number of particles and proteins which have been tested.

TABLE 4.4. *Distributions of some particles in the dextran–polyethylene glycol and the potassium phosphate–polyethylene glycol systems with different fractions of the polymers. B and T indicate that the particles or proteins favour the bottom and top phase respectively, I that some of the particles collect at the interface.*

Phase system	Starch particles	Cellulose particles	Chlorella	Erythro- cytes	Phyco- erythrin	Hemo- globin
D 19 – PEG 6 000	B	B	B	B	T	B
D 24 – PEG 6 000	B	B	B	B	T	B
D 37 – PEG 6 000	B	B	B	BI	T	B
D 48 – PEG 6 000	B	B	T	I	T	B
D 68 – PEG 6 000	B	B	T	I	T	B
D 68 – PEG 4 000	B	B	T	TI	T	B
D 68 – PEG 20 000	B	B	B	B	B	B
Potassium phosphate – PEG 200	B	B	T	T	T	T
– PEG 300	B	B	T	T	T	T
– PEG 400	B	B	T	T	T	T
– PEG 600	B	B	T	I	T	BT
– PEG 1 000	B	B	TI	I	T	BT
– PEG 1 540	B	B	B	B	T	B
– PEG 4 000	B	B	B	B	T	B
– PEG 6 000	B	B	B	B	T	B
– PEG 20 000	B	B	B	B	T	B

TABLE 4.5. *Partition coefficient of phycoerythrin and human serum albumin in the dextran–polyethylene glycol system with the same polymer composition (8% (w/w) dextran and 6% (w/w) polyethylene glycol), but with different fractions of the two polymers. Buffer: 0.005 M KH_2PO_4 + 0.005 M K_2HPO_4. Temperature: 20°C.*

	Partition coefficient	
Phase system	Phycoerythrin	Serum albumin
D 19 – PEG 6000	1.85	0.19
D 24 – PEG 6000	2.89	0.22
D 37 – PEG 6000	6.2	0.20
D 48 – PEG 6000	11.5	0.30
D 68 – PEG 6000	42.3	0.61
D 48 – PEG 4000	18.8	0.92

TABLE 4.6. *Distribution of particles in the dextran–methylcellulose system D 68 – MC 4000. The bottom phase is the dextran-rich phase and the top phase the methylcellulose-rich phase.*

Particle	Phase in which particles are collected
Starch grains	Bottom
Cellulose powder	Top
Polystyrene latex	Top
Chlorella	Bottom
E. coli	Bottom
Erythrocytes	Bottom
Penicillium spores	Interface
Particles from heat denatured hemoglobin	Top

4. EXPERIMENTS WITH THE DEXTRAN–METHYL-CELLULOSE SYSTEM (D68–MC4000)

Larger Particles and Whole Cells

In the dextran–methylcellulose system, large particles having a size greater than 0.1 μ usually give a completely unilateral distribution and interfacial adsorption seldom occurs. As may be seen in Table 4.6, most cells favour the dextran phase (bottom phase) except the *Penicillium* spores which are adsorbed to the interface. The particles preferring the top phase include polystyrene latex, cellulose particles, and particles of denatured protein such as heat-denatured hemoglobin.

Viruses

The distribution of protein molecules, or smaller particles such as those of viruses and microsomes, is entirely within the bulk phases and can be expressed in terms of a finite partition coefficient which can be measured. Viruses are particularly useful for studying the distributional behaviour of particles as they can be measured fairly accurately by specific methods depending on their infectivity. Thus very small or very large partition coefficients may be measured even in the presence of non-active impurities.

The partition coefficients of a number of viruses, having different shapes and sizes in the dextran–methylcellulose system D 68–MC 4000, are given in Table 4.7. The experiments were carried out employing two systems (4).

The first system, A1, has a polymer composition of 0.68 per cent (w/w) D 68 and 0.36 per cent (w/w) MC 4000. The composition of the phases at 4°C are given in Fig. 2.27. The volume of the top phase of this system is about three times larger than the bottom phase.

The second system, A2, has the same phase compositions as A1 but a different volume ratio, the bottom phase being about six times larger than the top phase. To obtain this system, 20 g of fresh bottom phase of system A1 are added to 5 g of system A1 containing the particles.

As examples, details of the experiments in the two systems will now be given:

A partition experiment with system A1 was carried out as follows. 36 g of a 1 per cent (w/w) solution of MC 4000, 6.8 g of a 10 per cent (w/w) solution of D 68, 15 g 1 M NaCl, 10 g 0.1 M buffer, and 12.2 g H_2O (total = 80 g) were weighed into a flask. This stock mixture was kept in the cold; under sterile conditions it keeps for several weeks. 4 parts by weight of this stock mixture were diluted with 1 part by weight of particle suspension to give the desired phase system A1. The flask containing the stock mixture was gently shaken to mix the two phases and a sample immediately withdrawn using a pipette with a wide orifice. 4 g of the stock mixture were then weighed into a tube, 7 cm long and 1 cm in diameter and 1 g of the protein solution or virus particle suspension added to the tube. The tube and contents were cooled to 4°C, then inverted about 50 times and allowed to stand for

48 hours for phase separation. A sample of 0.5–1 ml of the top phase was removed with a pipette and an equal amount of the bottom phase was carefully withdrawn by dipping a narrow pipette through the top phase down into the lower part of the bottom phase.

A partition experiment with system A2 was as follows. First, a suitable amount of system A1 was prepared, without particles or proteins but with the same salt and buffer content as the previous experiment and allowed to stand for phase separation. The bottom phase was collected and 20 g of this weighed into a tube 13 cm long and 1.7 cm in diameter. 4 g of the stock mixture described above, and 1 g of a virus particle suspension or protein solution were added to this tube. The contents were mixed and the experiment continued as for system A1.

As may be seen in Table 4.7 where the viruses are listed in order of their size, the larger the particle size the smaller the partition coefficient. In order to analyse these experimental data in terms of theory (page 100), the surface area of the particles has been computed from the shapes and dimensions of the particles as obtained from measurements with the electron microscope. This calculation was done in the following way (4).

For hemocyanin the data of Schramm & Berger (26) were used. The two types of hemocyanin molecule at pH 4.7–7.0 and 8.2–9.3 were both assumed to be rectangular parallelepipeds, with sides $40 \times 20 \times 10$ mμ for the whole molecule (pH = 6.2) and $20 \times 10 \times 5$ mμ for the "one-eighth" molecule (pH = 8.2).

Phycoerythrin has a molecular weight of 290,000 (28); its molecules were assumed to be spheres of diameter 10 mμ.

The tobacco mosaic virus particles were assumed to be cylinders 300 mμ long and 15 mμ in diameter (7).

The vaccinia virus particles were assumed to be spheres with a diameter of about 260 mμ (32).

The form and dimensions of the bacteriophages T2, T3 and T4 have been studied by Williams & Fraser (33) who concluded that the heads of all three phages are probably either rhombic dodecahedrons or hexagonal prisms with bipyramidal ends. The latter alternative was chosen. The tails have been treated as cylinders. For T3 the distance between parallel sides is 47 mμ. All sides of both the prism and the pyramids are of an equal length ($47/\sqrt{3}$ mμ). The cylinder is 15 mμ

119

TABLE 4.7. *The partition coefficient, K, and the surface area of a number of virus particles and protein molecules in the dextran–methylcellulose system D 68 – MC 4000 at 4°C. The polymer composition of this phase system is given in Fig. 2.27 (system A1). System A2 has an identical phase composition to A1, but a different volume ratio. FB = phosphate buffer. (The titre determinations of ECHO virus and polio virus were kindly carried out by Drs. L. Philipson and E. Norrby.)*

Particle	Surface area $(m\mu)^2$ $\times 10^{-3}$	K System A1	System A2	pH	Salt content	Reference
Phycoerythrin	0.3	0.95	0.95	6.8	0.01 M NaFB 0.15 M NaCl	
Hemocyanin "eighth"	0.86	0.65	0.62	8.4	0.01 M Tris-HCl 0.15 M NaCl	4
Hemocyanin "whole"	3.5	0.25		5.8	0.01 M NaFB 0.15 M NaCl	4
Echo virus	1.3	0.3	0.2	7	0.01 M NaFB 0.15 M NaCl	
Polio virus	2.3	0.2		7	0.01 M NaFB 0.15 M NaCl	
Phage T3	8.7	$2.1 \cdot 10^{-2}$	$2.3 \cdot 10^{-2}$	6.6	0.01 M NaFB 0.15 M NaCl	4
Tobacco mosaic virus	14.4	$(1-2)10^{-2}$		7.1	0.01 M NaFB	4
Phage T2	25.5	$2.6 \cdot 10^{-3}$	$(6-10)10^{-4}$	5.7–7.3	0.01 M NaFB 0.15 M NaCl	4
Phage T4	25.5	$2.5 \cdot 10^{-3}$	$(3-5)10^{-4}$	6.9	0.01 M NaFB 0.15 M NaCl	4
Vaccinia	220	$(1-3)10^{-3}$	$(4-12)10^{-5}$	7	0.01 M NaFB 0.15 M NaCl	4
Vaccinia		$(1-3)10^{-4}$		7	0.01 M NaFB 0.15 M NaCl	31

long and 10 mμ in diameter. For T2 and T4 the maximum length of the head is 95 mμ and the maximum width 65 mμ. The ratio between the length of the prism and the side of the pyramids is 3:2. The tail is 100 mμ long and 25 mμ in diameter.

The ECHO virus particles were assumed to be spheres of diameter 20 mμ (18).

The polio virus particles were also treated as spheres with a diameter of 27 mμ (25).

As may be seen in Fig. 4.4, where the logarithms of the K values of the different particles are plotted against their calculated surface

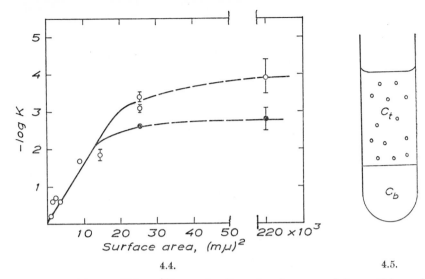

4.4.   4.5.

Fig. 4.4. Partition coefficients, K, as a function of surface area of the particles and molecules of some viruses and proteins in two dextran–methylcellulose systems. ●, in system A1, ○, in system A2; see Table 4.7.

Fig. 4.5. A phase system in which a part of the bottom phase remains as droplets in the top phase after the main bulk of the two phases has separated.

areas, the points cluster along a line up to a $-\log K$ value of 2 in system A1 and of 3 in system A2. This means that in the dextran–methylcellulose system and for the particles studied here, the surface area is the main factor determining the partition coefficient. For these particles in this system the factor λ in the Brønsted formula (page 100) may be therefore regarded as approximately a constant, that is the particles behave as if they have roughly the same surface properties.

For particles larger than phage T2, a linear relationship no longer holds; a limiting value of $-\log K$ is obtained for each system. Thus a K value less than 0.001 in system A1 and less than 0.0001 in system A2 has not been obtained even when larger virus particles or even whole cells have been tested.

These upper limit values of $-\log K$ in Fig. 4.4 can be explained as due to incomplete separation of the two phases. If small drops of the virus-rich bottom phase remain in the top phase when samples from this are withdrawn, the observed virus concentration in the top phase will be too high. Consider, for example, Fig. 4.5, which shows a phase system in which part of the bottom phase remains in the top phase in the form of droplets. Let the concentration of virus particles in the top and bottom phases be C_t and C_b respectively and the partition coefficient K. If a sample of volume V is drawn from the top layer, this will include top phase and a small volume of the bottom phase as droplets; let this latter volume be v. The measured concentration of virus particles in the sample from the top layer will then be

$$\frac{(V-v)\,C_t + v\,C_b}{V} \tag{2}$$

and the erroneously measured partition coefficient, which may be called an apparent partition coefficient and denoted as K', will thus be

$$K' = \frac{(V-v)\,C_t + v\,C_b}{V\,C_b}. \tag{3}$$

By inserting $K = C_t/C_b$ we obtain

$$K' = K + \frac{v}{V}(1 - K). \tag{4}$$

If the K value is made progressively smaller the limiting value is:

$$K' = \frac{v}{V}. \tag{5}$$

The K values of phage T2 and T4 and vaccinia virus in system A1 and the K values of vaccinia virus in system A2 given in Table 4.7 are, according to this explanation, almost entirely dominated by the droplet effect and merely expressions for the value of v/V in eqn (5). The difference between the two systems may be explained as due to the different volume ratios. The volume of the bottom phase of system A2 is thus about six times larger than that of the top phase, while in system A1 the bottom phase is only about one-third of the volume of the top phase. As mentioned in Chapter 2, the formation of droplets in the phases depends on the volume ratio so that, if one phase is small compared to the other, the smaller phase appears much clearer optically while the larger phase contains droplets of the other phase (Fig. 2.53). It is therefore highly probable that system A2 contains a smaller amount of droplets than system A1, that is v/V in eqn. (5) is smaller for system A2 than for A1.

Proteins

All proteins studied distribute rather evenly in the dextran–methylcellulose systems; they have, for example, partition coefficients close to unity (0.95–1) in the system as described above for viruses (Table 4.7), that is system A1 in Fig. 2.26. In order to compare different proteins and to study the influence of salt and pH, a number of proteins have therefore been distributed in system C of the system D68–MC4000 (see Fig. 2.26), which is further removed from the critical point. The results are given in Figs. 4.6–4.11 and in Table 4.8.

The partition coefficient of phycoerythrin in system C in the presence of different buffers is plotted as a function of pH in Fig. 4.6. As may be seen, different K values are obtained at the same pH when different kinds of buffers are used. This specific ionic effect may be almost completely supressed, however, by the addition of an excess of a neutral salt such as NaCl or KCl. Thus, the K values of Fig. 4.7 have been obtained in system C with the same buffer concentrations (0.01 M) as in Fig. 4.6, but with the addition of 0.1 M NaCl. The K value is then fairly constant in the pH region 4.5–10. At pH values below 4.25 (the isoelectric point) the protein is more or less precipitated. The small fraction of the protein which still remains in solution shows very high K values in the pH region 2–4; at pH values above 10 there is also an increase in the K value. At these high pH values the protein

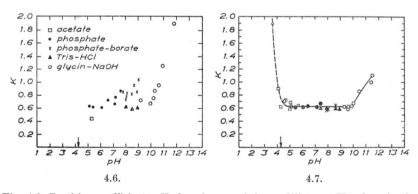

4.6.   4.7.

Fig. 4.6. Partition coefficients, K, for phycoerythrin at different pH values in the dextran–methylcellulose system D68–MC4000, (system C of Fig. 2.26). Buffer concentration 0.01 M, temperature 20°C. The arrow indicates the isoelectric point of phycoerythrin. The concentration of phycoerythrin was measured by its extinction at 495 mμ.

Fig. 4.7. The partition of phycoerythrin in the same system and with the same buffers as in Fig. 4.6, but with the addition of 0.1 M NaCl.

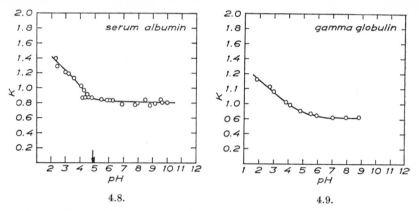

4.8.   4.9.

Fig. 4.8. Partition of human serum albumin in the same system as in Fig. 4.7, in 0.01 M buffer and 0.1 M NaCl. The arrow indicates the isoelectric point. The concentration of serum albumin was measured by its extinction at 280 mμ and by the method of Lowry *et al.* (see ref. 5 in Chapter 6). Buffers: glycine-HCl, pH 2–3.5; Na acetate, pH 4–5.5; Na phosphate, pH 5.5–7.5; Tris-HCl, pH 8–9; glycine-NaOH, pH 9–10. Temperature: 20°C.

Fig. 4.9. Partition of human gamma globulin in the same system as in Fig. 7, in 0.01 M buffer and 0.1 M NaCl. The concentration of gamma globulin was determined by the Kjeldahl method. Buffers: HCl–KCl, pH 1–3; Na acetate, pH 3.5–4.8; Na phosphate, pH 4.8–7; Na phosphate-borate, pH 7–9. Temperature: 20°C.

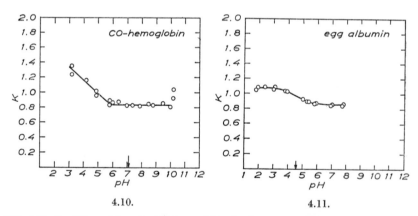

4.10.   4.11.

Fig. 4.10. Partition of human CO-hemoglobin in the same system as in Fig. 4.7, in 0.01 M buffer and 0.1 M NaCl. The CO-hemoglobin concentration was measured by its extinction at 540 mμ and 280 mμ. Buffers: HCl-glycine, pH 3–4.5; Na-acetate pH 4.5–5.8; Na phosphate, pH 6–7.5; Tris-HCl, pH 7.5–9; glycine-NaOH, pH 9–12. Temperature: 20°C.

Fig. 4.11. Partition of egg albumin in the same system as in Fig. 4.7, in 0.01 M buffer and 0.1 M NaCl. The concentration of protein was determined by the Kjeldahl method. Buffers: HCl–KCl, pH 1–3.5; Na phosphate, pH 3.8–8. Temperature: 20°C.

124

TABLE 4.8. *Partition coefficients, K, for various proteins in the dextran–methyl-cellulose system* D 68 – MC 4000 *(system C: see Fig. 2.26), at 20°C and in 0.01 M buffer and 0.1 M NaCl. The partition coefficient of egg albumin, CO-hemoglobin, serum albumin, gamma globulin and phycoerythrin are means of the values in the respective pH interval: see Figs. 4.7–11.*

Protein	Molecular weight	K	pH
Ribonuclease	13 000	1.0	7
Cytochrome C	16 000	1.0	7
Insulin		1.0	8.7
Pepsin		1.0	7
Pepsin	36 000	1.6	4
Egg albumin	44 000	0.87	5.3–8
CO-hemoglobin (human)	67 000	0.83	6–10
Serum albumin (human)	69 000	0.81	5–10
Gamma globulin (human)	156 000	0.64	5–9
Phycoerythrin	290 000	0.63	4.3–10
Hemocyanin, "eighth"	1 000 000	0.12	8.2
Hemocyanin, "whole"	9 000 000	< 0.01	6.0

is denatured; the colour partly disappears and ultracentrifugation reveals that the molecules are split (14).

A similar experiment with human serum albumin in 0.1 M NaCl is shown in Fig. 4.8, where the K value is fairly constant in the pH region 5–10 but outside this region the K values increase. Thus, the K values below pH 4 are even greater than unity, that is the protein partitions in favour of the top phase. Experiments with human gamma globulin, human CO-hemoglobin, and egg albumin are shown in Figs. 4.9–4.11. They show qualitatively the same results; the K values increase at lower pH values, below pH 5 for gamma globulin, below pH 6 for CO-hemoglobin, and below pH 5 for egg albumin, and become higher than unity.

The K values for a number of proteins in system C are given in Table 4.8. As can be seen, the K values decrease with increasing molecular size as was the case with viruses in system A1.

Finally, an experiment with *Helix pomatia* hemocyanin is summarized in Fig. 4.12. The protein was distributed in system B of the system D 68–MC 4000 (see Fig. 2.26) and the K value measured at different pH values in the presence of 0.1 M NaCl. *Helix pomatia* hemocyanin has been studied in detail with the ultracentrifuge (9, 28),

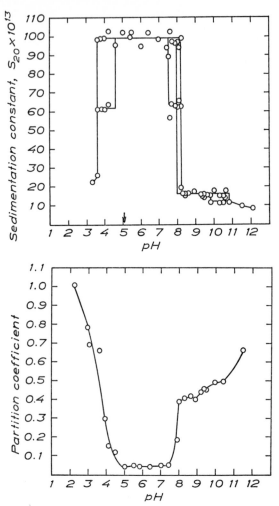

Fig. 4.12. Partition coefficients and sedimentation constants of *Helix pomatia* hemocyanin at different pH values. The partition coefficients were obtained in the dextran–methylcellulose system D68–MC4000 (system B in Fig. 2.26), in 0.01 M buffer and 0.1 M NaCl. Buffers: HCl–KCl, pH 2–3; glycine-HCl, pH 3–3.9; Na acetate, pH 3.9–5.5; Na phosphate, pH 5.8–7.5; Tris-HCl, pH 7.5–8.9; glycine-NaOH, pH 9–11.5. The sedimentation constants in the upper half of the figure have been obtained from ref. (28). The concentration of hemocyanin was determined by the method of Lowry *et al.*, see ref 5 in Chapter 6. Temperature: 20°C.

and from these studies the molecular weight as a function of pH is well known. In Fig. 4.12 the sedimentation constants (S_{20}) of the different molecular species present at various pH values are plotted for comparison with the K values of the protein in the phase system.

Thus, for pH 4.7–7.0 one component with $S_{20} = 100$, corresponding to a molecular weight of 9×10^6, is observed in the ultracentrifuge and in about the same pH region the K value is constant. At pH values between 7.4 and 8.2 the hemocyanin molecule dissociates into "half" and "eighth" molecules with $S_{20} = 60$ and 20 respectively, and in this pH region the K values increase. Between pH 8.2 and 9.3 there is only one component present with $S_{20} = 20$ and the K value is fairly constant between these pH values. At higher pH values the molecules are split into still smaller fragments and the K value then increases. At pH values between 4.7 and 3.6 the whole molecules are split into halves ($S_{20} = 60$) and the K value increases; below pH 3.6, the protein is split into a number of smaller fragments and the K value increases up to unity.

The K value of hemocyanin in the dextran–methylcellulose system, therefore, corresponds well with the behaviour of the protein in the ultracentrifuge. This is in agreement with what one would expect from the results with the other proteins and virus particles reported above, that is, the K value depends mainly upon the particle size of the partitioned substance and, within the stability region of protein, the K value is fairly constant at different pH values (in 0.01 M buffer and 0.1 M NaCl). The partition of hemocyanin differs in one respect from the partition of the other proteins: its K value does not become greater than unity at low pH values.

Nucleic Acids

The partition coefficients of some nucleic acid preparations are given in Table 4.9. They all partition in favour of the bottom phase. As was the case with viruses and proteins, the K values are smaller

TABLE 4.9. *Partition coefficient, K, and sedimentation constants, S_{20}, of some nucleic acid preparations. The K values were determined with the same phase system, A1, as Table 4.7, at $4°C$. From ref. (22).*

Nucleic acid	S_{20}	K
RNA from yeast	3.5	0.43
DNA from calf thymus (I)	20.4	0.017
DNA from calf thymus (II)	21.8	0.014

the larger the molecular size, that is, for those preparations with larger sedimentation constants.

The K values in system A1 for a nucleic acid and a protein with similar sedimentation constants differ considerably. Thus, the sedimentation constants for *Helix pomatia* hemocyanin at pH $= 8.2$ and DNA from thymus are about the same (20 S) while their K values are 0.85 and 0.017 respectively.

Influence of Temperature

The partition in the dextran–methylcellulose system is hardly affected by changes in temperature, as may be seen in Table 4.10 where the K values for hemocyanin and phages at 20°C and 4°C are given. This is probably due to the fact that the phase compositions of the dextran–methylcellulose system itself changes very little with changes in temperature (see Fig. 2.52).

TABLE 4.10. *Partition coefficients, K, at different temperatures for the dextran–methylcellulose system (system A1; Table 4.7). Data from ref. (4).*

| | K | |
Particle	4°C	20°C
Hemocyanin, "whole"	0.25	0.25
Tobacco mosaic virus	0.026	0.025
Phage T3	0.021	0.032
Phage T2	0.0026	0.0028

5. EXPERIMENTS WITH THE DEXTRAN-POLYETHYLENE GLYCOL SYSTEM

Whole Cells

Generally, larger particles such as whole cells seem to be more readily adsorbed at the interface of the dextran–polyethylene glycol system than the dextran–methylcellulose system. The distribution depends on the molecular weight of the polymer fraction used, as mentioned above (Table 4.4). A most striking characteristic of the dextran–polyethylene glycol system is the effect of salt. This is shown in Fig. 4.13 which records an experiment with *Chlorella* in the dextran–polyethylene glycol system D 48–PEG 6000. In the presence

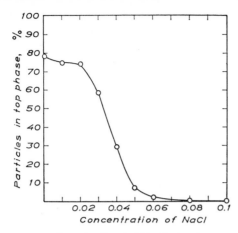

Fig. 4.13. Percentage number of cells of *Chlorella* in the top phase of the dextran–polyethylene glycol system 9 % (w/w) D 48 and 3 % (w/w) PEG 6000, in 0.01 M Na phosphate, pH = 6.8, and with increasing concentrations of NaCl. The latter is expressed as moles NaCl per 976 ml phase system. Temperature 20°C.

of 0.01 M Na phosphate, most of the cells were suspended in the top phase but if NaCl was added up to 0.1 M, all the particles became adsorbed at the interface. The percentage fraction of particles remaining suspended in the top phase is plotted as a function of the NaCl concentration in Fig. 4.13 where it can be seen that the curve is sigmoid and within a fairly narrow salt interval that the particles become transferred from the top phase to the interface. This is not merely due to the increase in ionic strength, since in 0.1 M sodium phosphate (pH = 6.8), all particles are still in the top phase; it is a specific effect caused by the addition of chloride ions to the system. Further, it seems to be the *ratio* between the concentration of the two salts, sodium phosphate and sodium chloride, rather than their individual concentrations which determines the distribution.

When different salts are tested it is found that each ion has a specific effect on the distribution. This is shown in Table 4.11 where the results from an experiment with *Chlorella* are given; the distribution was determined by visual inspection of the green colour. A similar salt effect has been observed on other particles and also on proteins. Since, for the latter a finite partition coefficient can be measured, the salt effect has only been studied quantitatively on proteins (see below) while the effect on the distribution of particles has been studied only qualitatively.

TABLE 4.11. *The distribution of Chlorella pyrenoidosa in the dextran–polyethylene glycol system, 7 % (w/w) D 48 and 4.4 % (w/w) PEG 6000, in the presence of 0.01 M phosphate buffer (pH = 6.8) and the salts listed. B and T indicate that almost all the cells go to the bottom phase or top phase respectively; when I is indicated together with B or T, some of the cells go to the interface. Concentration of the salts added: pyrophosphate 0.02 M, oxalate 0.01 M, the others 0.1 M.*

Salt	Distribution	Salt	Distribution
NaF	T	MgCl$_2$	I
NaCl	BI	Na$_2$SO$_4$	T
NaBr	BI	NaNO$_3$	BI
NaI	BI	Na pyrophos-	T
LiCl	T	phate, pH = 7	
KCl	BI	Na acetate	I
CsCl	BI	Na oxalate	T
		Na malonate	T
		Na succinate	TI
		Na citrate	T

The interface adsorption as a function of particle concentration

When the adsorption at the interface is studied as a function of the concentration of the distributed particles, different results are obtained for different particles. In Fig. 4.14 it may be seen that the amount of *Chlorella* adsorbed at the interface is directly proportional to the concentration of particles in the top phase (linear adsorption isotherm), a relation which holds up to fairly high concentration of cells; Fig. 4.14b. No deviation from this linear relation was found; it was not possible to introduce a larger amount of cells than that given in Fig. 4.14b since it then became too "thick". The measurements of the *Chlorella* concentration are also less accurate at higher concentrations, as is shown by the larger scatter of the points in Fig. 4.14b where the highest cell concentration was used. No precipitation or aggregation occurs when the *Chlorella* cells are added to the top phase alone.

A similar linear particle concentration dependence has also been found for starch particles (2) in a salt–polyethylene glycol system.

If the distribution of hemocyanin is tested at different concentrations, no such linear relation holds. Instead, the concentration of hemocyanin in the top phase remains approximately constant after a certain amount has been added. However, in contrast to *Chlorella*, a large part of the hemocyanin is precipitated if it is added into the

130

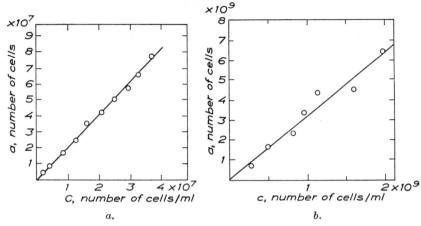

Fig. 4.14a. The number, a, of cells of *Chlorella* which collect at the interface as a function of the concentration of cells, c, in the top phase. The distribution was carried out
with a dextran–polyethylene glycol system having a polymer composition of 9 %
(w/w) D 48 and 3 % (w/w) PEG 6000 and with 0.005 M KH$_2$PO$_4$, 0.005 M K$_2$HPO$_4$,
and 0.03 M KCl. The volume of the top phase is 2.8 ml and the ratio between the
number of cells in the top phase and at the interface is 1.4. Temperature: 20°C.

b. As a, but in 0.05 M KCl and with higher concentrations of cells. 10^9 cells correspond
to about 10 mg dry weight of cells. The ratio of the number of cells in the top phase
to those at the interface is about 0.9. Due to the large number of cells attached to
the interface it becomes overloaded and material therefore passes into the bottom
phase.

top phase alone, that is the hemocyanin present at the interface may
be considered as a separate precipitated phase.

Viruses

Tobacco mosaic virus. The distribution of this virus in the dextran–
polyethylene glycol system D 48–PEG 6000 depends on the salt content in a similar manner to that described above for cells. Thus,
for example, in the presence of 0.01 M potassium phosphate pH = 7.5,
almost all the virus is in the top phase of a system with 7 per cent
(w/w) D 48 and 3 per cent (w/w) PEG 6000. If sodium chloride is
added, the virus is transferred to the interface so that in 0.1 M sodium
chloride in the same phase system, more than 90 per cent of the virus
is collected at the interface.

Animal viruses. A number of animal viruses have been tested in the
dextran–polyethylene glycol system (31). The activity of the top

TABLE 4.12. *Distribution of viruses in samples from the top phase (T), bottom phase (B), and interface (I) of the dextran–polyethylene glycol system 5 % (w/w) D 48 and 3 % (w/w) PEG 6000. The values given for vaccinia and Echo virus are log units of infectivity titres; the other values are dilution values of hemagglutination titres. From ref. (31).*

Salt	Echo 7			Vaccinia			Parotitis			Newcastle disease			Influenza		
	T	I	B	T	I	B	T	I	B	T	I	B	T	I	B
0.1 *M* Na phosphate pH = 7	5.5	6.9	5.9	2.9	6.1	4.5	2	64	16	32	128	16	16	64	16
0.1 *M* Na phosphate pH = 7 0.15 NaCl	5.5	6.5	6.9	2.7	6.5	4.1	4	64	16	32	128	16	4	64	32

phase, the bottom phase, and a sample from the interface was determined in systems with different polymer concentrations and salt contents. As may be seen in Table 4.12 where an experiment is given, the major part of the virus activity, except in the case of ECHO virus, was found in the sample from the interface. The remaining activity was greater in the bottom phase than the top phase. In the systems with 0.15 *M* sodium chloride, ECHO virus was partitioned in favour of the bottom phase. Of the viruses tested here, ECHO virus is a small virus with a particle diameter less than 25 mμ, while the other viruses are fairly large with particle diameters greater than 80 mμ.

Proteins

Usually most proteins with molecular weights less than about one million are dissolved in the dextran–polyethylene glycol system. As with whole cells, the distribution depends on the particular molecular weight fraction of the polymers (see Table 4.5) and also to a great extent on the salt content. Thus a protein may be transferred from one phase to the other simply by changing the ionic composition of the phase system. This salt effect has been studied in detail on a number of proteins (5, 6), and in this section these results together with others will be described.

The experiments were made with a system of 7 per cent (w/w) D 48 and 4.4 per cent (w/w) PEG 6000. When only water is present in addition to the polymers, this system is, in this section, called the standard phase system. 1 kg of the standard phase system has a volume of 0.976 litres. Its phase composition may be found from the phase diagram in Fig. 2.13. When salt is added to produce concentrations less than 1 M, one ml water of the phase system is replaced by one ml of the salt solution. The salt content will then be expressed as moles salt per 0.976 litre phase system, that is roughly molarity concentrations. The same applies to the addition of a protein solution.

If a salt, for example sodium chloride, is added to concentrations higher than 1 M, it is added dry to the standard phase system. The salt content is then expressed as moles salt added per kg standard phase system (or added per 0.976 litre standard phase system), that is roughly molality concentrations. When an experiment with the dextran–polyethylene glycol is described, M refers to moles per 976 ml standard phase system.

1. Influence of different salts on the distribution of phycoerythrin

The partition coefficient of phycoerythrin in the presence of 0.01 M potassium phosphate (equimolar parts of KH_2PO_4 and K_2HPO_4) and different salts is recorded in Fig. 4.15. In the buffer alone the protein is mainly in the top phase with a K value of about 7; see the broken line in Fig. 4.15. For the addition of the other salts, there is a definite corresponding K value which is always lower than that obtained in the buffer alone. This tendency of the salts to lower the K value is different for the different salts tested. Thus, ammonium sulfate or citrate hardly affect the K value, while potassium chloride or sodium nitrate reduce it to about 0.3 so that the major part of the protein is transferred to the bottom phase.

There seems to be a certain pattern regarding the ability of the different salts to lower the K values. As may be seen in Fig. 4.15, the potassium halogenides lower the K value in the following order $F^- < Cl^- < Br^- < I^-$, and the alkaline chlorides in the order $Li^+ < NH_4^+ < Na^+ \sim Cs^+ < K^+$. As Table 4.13 shows, the difference in effect between the ammonium and sodium ion is the same whether the anion is chloride, nitrate or sulfate. The difference in the effect of the two ions does not therefore seem to depend on the other ions present.

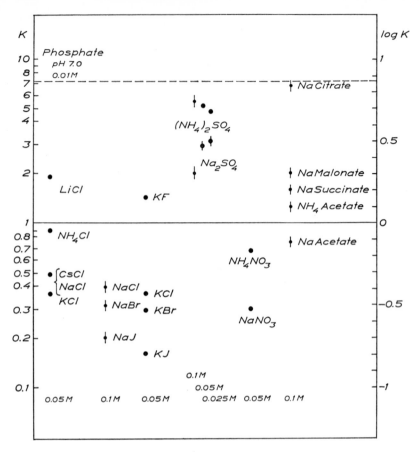

Fig. 4.15. Partition coefficients, K, of phycoerythrin in a dextran–polyethylene glycol system with 0.005 M KH_2PO_4 and 0.005 M K_2HPO_4, and different electrolytes; the concentrations of the latter are indicated in the bottom row. Polymer composition = 7 % (w/w) D 48; 4.4 % (w/w) PEG 6000. Temperature: 20°C. From ref. (6).

2. Influence of the concentration of ions on the distribution of proteins

Experiments with phycoerythrin in potassium phosphate

In Fig. 4.16 the K value of phycoerythrin is plotted against the ratio between the concentration of the two phosphates, KH_2PO_4 and K_2HPO_4. In the left-hand half of Fig. 4.16 the concentration of KH_2PO_4 remains constant (= 0.01 M) and the concentration of K_2HPO_4 is decreased from 0.01 to 0.0001 M. In the right half of the Fig. 4.16 the concentration of K_2HPO_4 is kept constant (= 0.01 M) and the concentration of KH_2PO_4 is decreased from 0.01 to 0.0001 M. The K value

TABLE 4.13. *Partition coefficient, K, of phycoerythrin in a dextran–polyethylene glycol system in the presence of 0.01 M potassium phosphate buffer pH = 6.8 and different sodium and ammonium salts. From ref. (6).*

Salt	Concentration M	K	$\log K$	Difference between $\log K$ in 0.05 M NH_4^+ and Na^+
$(NH_4)_2SO_4$	0.025	5.1	0.71	
Na_2SO_4	0.025	3.0	0.48	0.23
NH_4Cl	0.05	0.90	−0.05	
$NaCl$	0.05	0.49	−0.31	0.26
NH_4NO_3	0.05	0.68	−0.17	
$NaNO_3$	0.05	0.37	−0.43	0.26

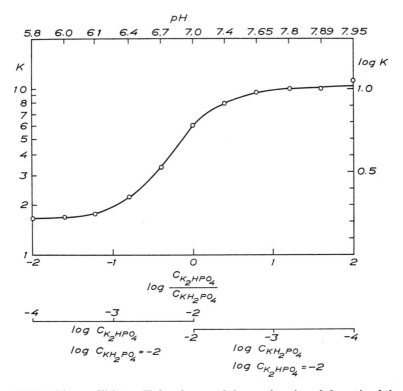

Fig. 4.16. Partition coefficients, K, for phycoerythrin as a function of the ratio of the concentrations of KH_2PO_4 and K_2HPO_4 in the dextran–polyethylene glycol system at 20°C. Polymer composition = 7 % (w/w) D 48; 4.4 % (w/w) PEG 6000. From ref. (6).

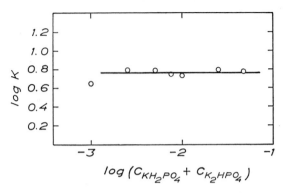

Fig. 4.17. As in Fig. 4.16, but with a constant ratio (1:1) between the concentrations of KH_2PO_4 and K_2HPO_4. From ref. (6).

remains fairly constant in the regions where one of the two salts is present in excess, that is at a concentration more than 10 times larger than the other salt.

If the ratio between the concentrations of KH_2PO_4 and K_2HPO_4 is constant, for example $= 1$ (pH ~ 7), but the concentrations are varied, the K value remains almost constant in the concentration range 0.001–0.05 and then increases; see Fig. 4.17.

Experiments with phycoerythrin in potassium phosphate +
potassium chloride

In Fig. 4.15 it was shown that the addition of potassium chloride to a system with phycoerythrin in potassium phosphate buffer lowers the K value. This effect has been studied at different concentrations of both the buffer and potassium chloride. In each experiment the concentration of the phosphate buffer (equimolar parts of KH_2PO_4 and K_2HPO_4) was kept constant and the potassium chloride concentration was varied from 1/100 to 100 times that of the phosphate buffer. The results are shown in Fig. 4.18, where the log K value of the protein has been plotted against the ratio of the concentration of potassium chloride and potassium phosphate buffer. The different K values cluster around a sigmoid curve, indicating that the K value is determined almost only by the *ratio* of the concentrations of the two salts. For a given concentration ratio, the K value is independent of the ionic strength up to 0.2 M. Fig. 4.18 also shows that if one salt has a concentration of more than 10 times that of the other salt, the K value is hardly affected even by changes in the ratio of the two salts.

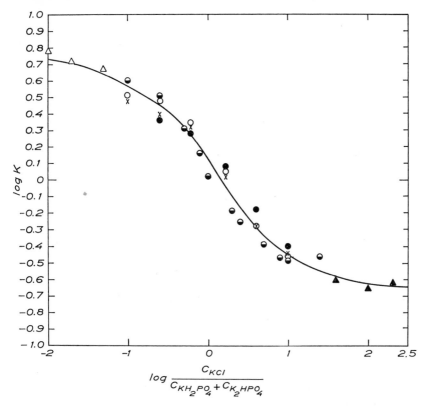

Fig. 4.18. Partition coefficients, K, as a function of the ratio of the concentrations of KCl and K phosphate. The phase system is identical to that in Fig. 4.16. Temperature: 20°C. From ref. (6). The following concentrations of $KH_2PO_4(=K_2HPO_4)$ were used: 0.00025 M (▲), 0.0005 M (●), 0.00125 M (×), 0.0025 M (○), 0.005 M (◑), 0.0125 M (△).

Experiments with different proteins in potassium phosphate

The partition of a number of proteins with increasing phosphate buffer concentration is shown in Fig. 4.19. In all experiments the concentrations of KH_2PO_4 and K_2HPO_4 were equimolar. Thus the experiments of Fig. 4.19 are similar to that with phycoerythrin shown in Fig. 4.17. For all proteins tested the K value remained fairly constant in the concentration range 0.004–0.1 M. At lower phosphate concentrations the K value decreases somewhat and at higher concentrations increases.

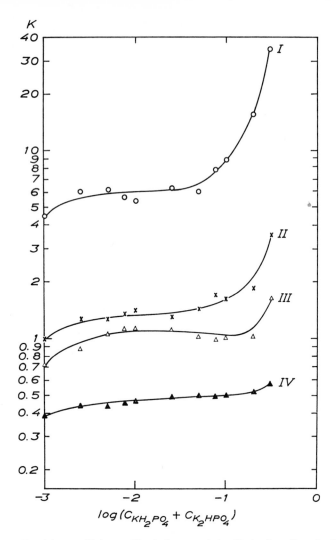

Fig. 4.19. Partition coefficients, K, of phycoerythrin (I), barley albumin (II), ceruloplasmin (III), and human serum albumin (IV) in the dextran–polyethylene glycol system with equimolar parts of KH_2PO_4 and K_2HPO_4 and the same polymer composition as in Fig. 4.15. Temperature: 20°C. From ref. (6).

Experiments with different proteins in potassium phosphate + potassium chloride or sodium chloride

The partition of a number of proteins in 0.01 M potassium phosphate (equimolar parts of KH_2PO_4 and K_2HPO_4) and increasing concentrations of potassium chloride is shown in Fig. 4.20. These

138

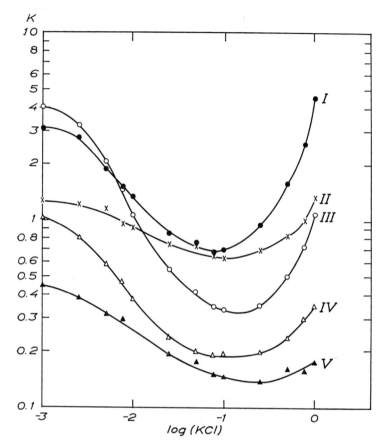

Fig. 4.20. Partition coefficients of phycocyanin (I), barley albumin (II), phycoerythrin (III), ceruloplasmin (IV), and human serum albumin (V), in the dextran–polyethylene glycol system with 0.005 M KH$_2$PO$_4$, 0.005 M K$_2$HPO$_4$, and increasing concentrations of KCl. The polymer composition is identical to that in Fig. 4.15. From ref. (5).

curves correspond to the curve of Fig. 4.18. They are of a similar shape for the different proteins; in all cases the addition of potassium chloride up to a concentration of 0.1–0.2 M lowers the K value. At higher concentrations the K value increases. Quantitatively, the effect of increasing the potassium chloride concentration is very different for the different proteins. The change in the K value of phycoerythrin and phycocyanin is, for example, much greater than that of serum albumin.

Unfortunately, the effect of potassium chloride at very high concentrations cannot be studied, since the dextran phase is transformed into

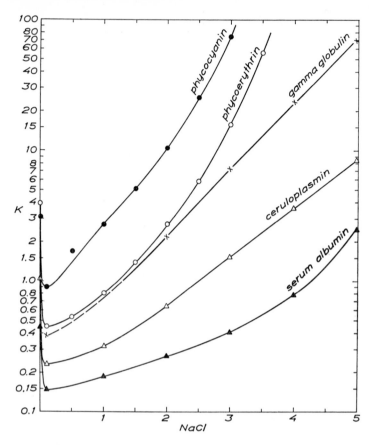

Fig. 4.21. Partition coefficients, K, of a number of proteins in the dextran–polyethylene glycol system in 0.005 M KH$_2$PO$_4$, 0.005 M K$_2$HPO$_4$ and with increasing concentration of NaCl; the latter is expressed as moles NaCl added per kg standard phase system. For the polymer and salt compositions of the phases, see Figs. 2.24 and 2.25.

a gel at high potassium chloride concentrations. This does not take place with sodium chloride and this salt was therefore chosen to study the partition of proteins at salt concentrations above 1 M. In this case the salt is added dry to the standard phase system. The polymer and salt compositions of the phases of these systems are given in Figs. 2.24 and 2.25. The results with some proteins are shown in Fig. 4.21. The concentration range between 0 and 1 M sodium chloride corresponds to that of Fig. 4.20. At higher concentrations the proteins are transferred to the top phase. The log K value for some proteins increase, approximately linearly, with the number of moles

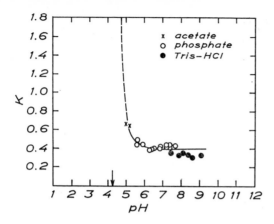

Fig. 4.22. Partition coefficients, K, of phycoerythrin at different pH values in a dextran–polyethylene glycol system with 0.01 M buffer and 0.2 M NaCl. The polymer composition are as in Fig. 4.15. The arrow indicates the isoelectric point. Compare with Figs. 4.16 and 4.7.

of sodium chloride added per kg standard phase system. This increase is very different for different proteins; the log K values become increasingly divergent as the salt concentration is raised. For fractionation purposes the conditions therefore improve as more salt is added. The three serum proteins, serum albumin, ceruloplasmin, and gamma globulin, for example, have not very different K values at 0.1 M NaCl ($K = 0.15$, 0.23, and 0.38 respectively) while, after 3 moles NaCl have been added, the K value of serum albumin is 0.4, that of ceruloplasmin 1.5, and that of gamma globulin 7. The separation effect is still greater if the polymer composition is further removed from the critical point.

3. *Phycoerythrin and serum albumin at different pH values*

The partition of phycoerythrin in phosphate buffer at different pH values has been given in Fig. 4.16. In analogy with experiments with the dextran–methylcellulose system (Fig. 4.6 and 4.7), the partition of phycoerythrin and serum albumin has been studied in different buffers (0.01 M) with an excess of a neutral salt (0.1–0.2 M NaCl). As may be seen in Fig. 4.22, the variation in the K value of phycoerythrin in the pH region 5.5–9 is not great.

When phosphate buffers are used in 0.2 M NaCl, the K value is

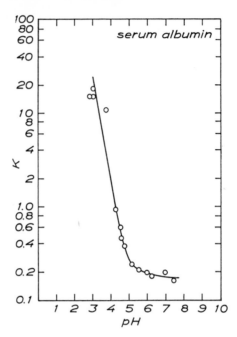

Fig. 4.23. Partition coefficients, K, for human serum albumin in the dextran–poly-ethylene glycol system with 0.01 M buffer and 0.1 M NaCl; polymer compositions are as in Fig. 4.15; buffers: HCl–KCl, pH 2–4; Na acetate, pH 4–5.5; Na phosphate, 5.5–7; Tris–HCl 7–8. The arrow indicates the isoelectric point. Compare this figure with Fig. 4.8.

constant for pH 5.9–7.6. Thus, comparing the curve of Fig. 4.16, where phosphate buffer without added neutral salt was used, with the curve of Fig. 4.22, it is evident that the variations in the K value caused by different molar proportions of KH_2PO_4 and K_2HPO_4 are completely removed when excess sodium chloride is added. Again the result is thus obtained, that if one salt is present in excess, that is it has a concentration 10 times or more that of the other salts, variations in the absolute concentration of these salts do not affect the K value to any great extent. At pH values below 5, most of the phycoerythrin precipitates; the small fraction remaining in solution has a high K value; compare with Fig. 4.7.

The K value of serum albumin as a function of pH in 0.1 M NaCl is shown in Fig. 4.23. The K value is constant between the pH values 5 and 8, at lower pH values it increases, and becomes larger than unity at pH values lower than 4.2. This behaviour is qualitatively similar

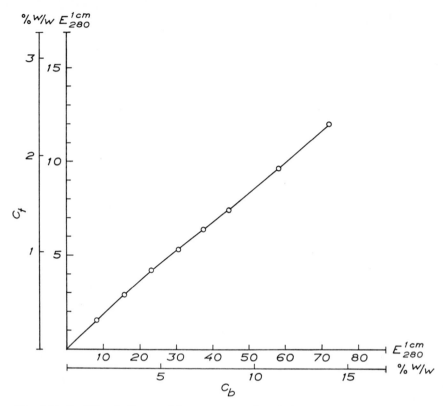

Fig. 4.24. Partition isotherm of human serum albumin in the dextran–polyethylene glycol system, 7 % (w/w) D48, 4.4 % (w/w) PEG 6000, 0.01 M Na phosphate, pH = 6.8, and 0.1 M NaCl, at 20°C. C_b and C_t = concentration of serum albumin in bottom and top phase respectively.

to the partition of serum albumin in the dextran–methylcellulose system (Fig. 4.8) but the change in the K value is much more drastic in the dextran–polyethylene glycol system.

4. *Dependence on protein concentration*

The K value as a function of the protein concentration has not been studied on a large number of proteins. Countercurrent experiments indicate, however, that the K value is constant at different protein concentrations, even at fairly high concentrations, and independent of the presence of other proteins; see Chapter 5. An experiment with serum albumin at high concentrations is shown in

Fig. 4.24. The partition isotherm is linear up to about 5 per cent serum albumin in the bottom phase and deviates only slightly from linearity at higher concentrations.

6. EXPERIMENTS WITH THE Na DEXTRAN SULFATE-METHYLCELLULOSE SYSTEM

Larger particles, such as whole cells, become distributed unilaterally, while proteins have a more even distribution with partition coefficients about unity. In this respect the distribution in the dextran sulfate–methylcellulose system resembles that in the dextran–methylcellulose system.

Only viruses and nucleic acids have been studied quantitatively in the dextran sulfate–methylcellulose system.

TABLE 4.14. *Partition coefficients, K, of some viruses in a Na dextran sulfate–methylcellulose system containing 0.40 % (w/w) of NaDS 68 and 0.48 % (w/w) MC 4000, in 0.15 M NaCl at 4°C. Data from ref. (24).*

Virus	K
ECHO	$10^{-0.4}$
Influenza	$10^{-2.3}$
Adeno	$10^{-2.8}$
Phage T2	$10^{-2.6}$

Viruses

The distribution of some viruses is shown in Table 4.14 where it can be seen that all viruses, except ECHO virus which has a small particle diameter, are concentrated in the bottom phase (24).

Nucleic Acids

The distribution of some nucleic acid preparations is given in Table 4.15. Highly polymerized deoxyribonucleic acid (DNA), such as thymus DNA and phage T2 DNA, collects predominantly at the interface of the dextran sulfate–methylcellulose system (22). This behaviour is different from the distribution in the dextran–methylcellulose system where all DNA is in the bulk phases, no significant amount being present at the interface (see Table 4.9).

TABLE 4.15. *Distribution of some nucleic acid preparations in a Na dextran sulfate–methylcellulose system with 0.70 % (w/w) NaDS 68 and 0.25 (w/w) MC 4000 in 0.005 M NaH_2PO_4, 0.005 M Na_2HPO_4, and 0.3 M NaCl at 4°C. C_t = concentration in top phase, C_b = concentration in bottom phase, V_b = volume of bottom phase, a = amount of nucleic acid collected at the interface. The concentration of nucleic acid was about 1 mg per 10 g phase system. Data from ref. (22).*

Nucleic acid	S_{20}	$\dfrac{C_t}{C_b + a/V_b}$
RNA from yeast	3.5	0.67
DNA from calf thymus (I)	20.4	0.17
DNA from calf thymus (II)	21.8	0.14
DNA from calf thymus (III)	22.5	0.12
DNA from phage T2 (I)	31.1	0.01
DNA from phage T2 (II)	31.5	0.08
DNA from phage T2 (III)	33.0	0.02

The collection of DNA at the interface of the Na dextran sulfate–methylcellulose system is at least partly a result of low solubility in the phases, since a partial precipitation of DNA is obtained in a dextran sulfate solution of the same concentration as the bottom phase (22). The quotient of the concentration of DNA in the top phase and the amount of DNA present at the interface and bottom phase depends in a regular manner on the size of the DNA molecules. This is shown by Table 4.15, the ratio becoming less the larger the sedimentation constant.

7. EXPERIMENTS WITH THE Na DEXTRAN SULFATE–POLYETHYLENE GLYCOL SYSTEM

Viruses

The partition of a number of viruses (24) in different Na dextran sulfate–polyethylene glycol systems with varying salt concentrations is shown in Table 4.16. The approximate composition of the phases of the different systems may be found in Figs. 2.33 and 2.34. As may be seen in Table 4.16, there is a general tendency for all viruses to partition in favour of the top phase at higher salt concentrations; in 0.15 M NaCl all viruses collect in the bottom phase, while in 1 M NaCl they are found in the top phase. In systems with intermediate

TABLE 4.16. *Partition coefficients, K, of some viruses in Na dextran sulfate–polyethylene glycol systems with varying concentrations of NaCl. Data from ref. (24).*

Phase system			K			
NaDS 68 % (w/w)	PEG 6000 % (w/w)	NaCl molarity	ECHO 7	ECHO 19	Adeno virus	Phage T2
4.8	1.4	1.0	$10^{2.6}$	$10^{2.8}$	$10^{0.2}$	
3.0	2.0	1.0	$10^{0.4-0.8}$ (I)	$10^{2.2}$	$10^{1.2}$	$10^{2.75}$
3.0	3.0	0.5	$10^{-0.4}$	$10^{0.2}$	$10^{1.2}$	$10^{0.8}$ (I)
4.0	4.0	0.3	$10^{-2.0}$	$10^{-1.1}$	$10^{0-0.6}$ (I)	
6.0	7.0	0.15	$10^{-2.2}$	$10^{-2.2}$	$10^{-2.6}$ (I)	$10^{-2.45}$

NaCl concentrations, the viruses differ in their behaviour. Thus, adeno virus and phage T2 are adsorbed partly at the interface while ECHO virus is not. The results of the partition shown in Table 4.16 have been used for the construction of phase systems for the purification and concentration of viruses; see Chapter 7.

Proteins and Nucleic Acids

Like viruses, proteins and nucleic acids shift phase when the NaCl concentration is increased from 0.15 to 1 *M*. Quantitatively, they differ in their behaviour; most proteins dissolve in the Na dextran sulfate–polyethylene glycol system, while a major part of thymus DNA collects at the interface. The latter behaviour is in contrast to the dextran–polyethylene glycol system where no adsorption of DNA at the interface takes place.

DISCUSSION

The experiments described in this chapter were primarily carried out to find out if there is any regularity in the behaviour of particles and macromolecules in aqueous polymer–polymer phase systems which might be of practical value for the construction of phase systems suitable for characterization and fractionation. The results are also of theoretical interest, however, and give information on the interaction between proteins, polymers, and electrolytes. In the discussion below, the results will also be compared with the particle behaviour predictable from the theory of Chapter 3.

The distribution behaviour of particles and macromolecules has been thoroughly studied only in a few of the very large number of possible polymer–polymer phase systems. Thus, most of the results have been obtained from experiments with the dextran–methylcellulose and the dextran–polyethylene glycol systems. The results from these systems will therefore be discussed separately.

Denaturation and Dissolving Power

No sign of denaturation, causing a loss in biological activity such as enzyme activity or virus infectivity, change in colour or solubility, has so far been encountered when the partition is carried out at a suitable pH or salt concentration. The enzymes tested include enolase (3), ceruloplasmin (5), laccase (3), and xanthine oxidase (8), and the viruses tested include bacteriophages T2, T4, and T3 (4), and a large number of animal viruses. (24, 31). The dextran–methylcellulose system permits distribution studies on the largest number of macromolecules without precipitation. All proteins so far tested, including fibrinogen, dissolve and even such labile colloids as the lipoproteins from serum remain suspended in this system which has the highest water content (98–99 per cent) of the systems studied.

The dextran–polyethylene glycol system has less dissolving power and contains less water (80–95 per cent). Thus, in the dextran–polyethylene glycol system, D 48–PEG 6000, a major part of lipoproteins and fibrinogen from serum are precipitated and collect at the interface. A small fraction of gamma globulin is also precipitated at the interface in 0.1–2 M salt concentrations. At higher salt concentrations, all gamma globulin dissolves in the phases. Except for these instances, all proteins so far studied with a molecular weight less than about 1 million, dissolve in the dextran–polyethylene glycol system. Proteins having a molecular weight larger than about 1 million, such as hemocyanin, precipitate at the interface in some salt solutions. In the case of hemocyanin the precipitation at the interface involves no gross denaturation; if the precipitate is collected and dissolved in water the resulting solution has the same absorption spectrum and sedimentation behaviour as the original hemocyanin.

The polymer–polymer phase systems do not thus appear to affect the proteins irreversibly which is probably due mainly to the high water content (80–99 per cent) of *both* phases and the small liquid–liquid interfacial tension. However, the possibility that the presence of the polymers themselves stabilizes the proteins should also be considered. The polymers used are polysaccharides or poly-ols which are known to stabilize certain enzymes against inactivation. Thus, it has been reported in a number of papers (10, 15, 19, 20, 21) that many enzymes and proteins are stabilized against heat denaturation or freeze drying by such substances as glycerol, glucose, sucrose, starch, dextrins, amino acids, and proteins. Viruses are stabilized against gas-liquid interface inactivation, by gelatin and proteins (1). Proteins also protect viruses against inactivation when subjected to sonic treatment (1).

The protective effect of some polymers used here may be easily demonstrated on egg albumin which is rather sensitive to surface denaturation. If a test tube containing a solution of egg albumin is shaken for a while, the solution becomes turbid due to precipitated denatured egg albumin. If, however, methylcellulose or polyethylene glycol are previously added, the solution remains clear even after prolonged, vigorous shaking (Fig. 4.25). This protective effect of the polymers is particularly useful when a large number of shakings are necessary for an experiment involving use of a countercurrent distribution apparatus.

Distribution in Systems with Compositions More or Less Removed from the Critical Point

The main conclusion to be drawn from the experiments of section 2 and those reported previously (30), is that a substance is distributed more unilaterally, and has a greater tendency to be adsorbed at the interface, the further the system lies from the critical point. Qualitatively, these results are in agreement with the theory for the distribution of particles in two-phase systems oulined in Chapter 3. Thus, the difference in properties between the two phases is greater in systems far from the critical point than those close to it. This usually implies that γ_{12}, and for most particles the difference $\gamma_{P1}-\gamma_{P2}$, is greater for systems well removed from the critical point than those near to it. From eqn. 17 of Chapter 3, a more unilateral distribution would be

148

| 1 | 2 | 3 | 4 | 5 |

Fig. 4.25. Protective effect of polymers on the denaturation of egg albumin caused by shaking. The tubes contain the following solutions. 1, egg albumin. 2, egg albumin after vigorous shaking; precipitated denatured protein is visible. 3, egg albumin plus methylcellulose (MC 4000) after vigorous shaking; no precipitation. 4, egg albumin plus polyethylene glycol (PEG 6000) after vigorous shaking; no precipitation. 5, egg albumin plus dextran after vigorous shaking: precipitation as in 2; dextran has no protective effect.

expected for the former systems and this is also found in practice. There should also be a greater tendency for adsorption at the interface for systems with larger interfacial tensions; eqns. 20 and 21 of Chapter 3. This is also the case in practice, adsorption of particles at the interface occurring more frequently in systems far from the critical point (Table 4.3).

Influence of the Properties of the Polymers

Non-polar groups. It is difficult to compare different phase systems as regards the concentration of non-polar groups in the phases because there are so many other factors (size and structure of the polymers, electrolytes) which influence the distribution. Also, the difference in the concentration of non-polar groups of two phases is comparatively small due to the low polymer concentration and the hydrophilic nature of the polymers. We may place the different polymers in the following series with decreasing polarity (or increasing hydrophobic character): Na dextran sulfate = Na carboxymethyldextran < dextran < hydroxypropyldextran < methylcellulose < polyvinylalcohol < polyethylene glycol < polypropylene glycol. Generally, most biological particles or macromolecules may be partitioned in favour of a phase containing any of these polymers except polypropylene glycol. In all phase systems containing a polypropylene glycol-rich phase, the particles favour the other phase.

Chain structure. The influence of the chain structure of the polymer molecules has not been studied systematically. It is considered, however, that it may have a great effect on the distribution of particles. This is shown by the following example on the distribution of cellulose particles and starch grains in a dextran–methylcellulose and a "soluble starch"–methylcellulose system:

If starch grains (for example from potatoe starch) and cellulose particles are shaken in a system of "soluble starch" and methylcellulose, both particles go to the bottom phase (the starch phase). This is as expected since both particle-types would favour the more hydrophilic bottom phase. However, if the two particles are distributed in a dextran–methylcellulose system the cellulose particles go to the top phase (the methylcellulose phase) while the starch grains go to the bottom phase. Thus, two polysaccharide particles which are chemically rather similar, have been completely separated using a two-phase system of two different polysaccharides. It seems reasonable to suppose that the cellulose particles favour the methylcellulose phase of the dextran–methylcellulose system because of a similarity in configuration of the methylcellulose molecules and the surface layer of the cellulose particles.

It would certainly be of great interest to study the effect of the configuration of the polymers in more detail and relate it to the structure of the surface of the particles. By using a number of polymers, mainly differing in chain configuration, it might be possible to obtain "stereospecific" separations. At the present stage, however, the available polymers do not permit such a study.

Molecular weight. The influence of the molecular weight of the polymers can be studied separately from other factors. In the three systems, 8 per cent (w/w) D 68, D 48, or D 37 and 6 per cent (w/w) PEG 6000, the phases have the same concentrations of polymers (see Fig. 2.54) and the distribution of electrolytes is also very similar; the electrolytes being almost equally distributed between the phases. Thus, the three systems differ mainly in the molecular weight of the dextran. The variation in the partition coefficient of the proteins given in Table 4.5 is therefore a direct effect of the change in molecular weight of dextran.

The fact that a solute is partly displaced from a phase if the polymer of this phase is replaced by a higher molecular weight fraction, is analogous to the effect of molecular weight on the mutual solubility of polymers. Thus, it is a general phenomenon that a macromolecule becomes less soluble in a solution of another macromolecule if the molecular weight of the latter is increased; see for example Figs. 2.49 and 2.50.

The Distribution in the Dextran–Methylcellulose System

If we consider the phase composition of this system (see Figs. 2.26 and 2.27), it is evident that the bottom phase contains 1–2 per cent dextran and 0.1–0.2 per cent methylcellulose in water and the top phase 0.2–0.5 per cent dextran and 0.5–1 per cent methylcellulose in water. When a salt is present, this distributes equally between the phases. Thus, the two phases differ chemically only in the slight difference in polymer composition. The top phase contains slightly more of the non-polar methyl groups. The chain configuration of the two polymers also differs, the methylcellulose molecules consisting of one chain while the dextran molecules are branched and thus more compact. This difference in structure is shown, for example, by the much higher viscosity of a methylcellulose solution compared to a dextran solution when both polymers have the same concentration and molecular weight.

The difference between the two phases of a dextran–methylcellulose system is therefore extremely small in comparison with other phase systems and this is reflected in the partition behaviour of proteins, which have about equal affinities for both phases, the K values being near unity.

Furthermore, as Tables 4.7–4.9 show, most proteins, all the virus particles and all the nucleic acids tested partition in favour of the bottom phase which contains the smaller concentration of methyl groups. Exceptions are pepsin and insulin at certain pH values and also many proteins at low or high pH values. Pepsin is in general an exceptional protein, a large number of its amino acids having hydrophobic side groups. Insulin has different molecular weights at different pH values and since the changes in the K values of insulin at different pH values are small due to its low molecular weight, the results on this protein are not accurate and difficult to interpret. In the case of the proteins (Fig. 4.8–4.11) which partition in favour of the top phase at low pH values, it is interesting to compare their K values, with their optical rotations and viscosities as functions of pH.

Thus, serum albumin shows a significant increase in the magnitude of its levorotation and also an increase in its limiting viscosity number below pH 4–4.5 (27, 29, 34). The same holds for gamma globulin at a pH below 4–4.5 or above 8.5–9. It has been suggested (16) that these changes in viscosity and optical rotation are the results of configurational changes of the protein molecules. The serum albumin molecule is thus considered to expand below pH 4 due to electrostatic repulsion forces and the loosening of internal bonds holding the "native" configuration of a neutral pH range. Also, as the protein molecule expands, several of its previously hidden hydrophobic groups become exposed. If this idea is correct, it would also explain the increases in the K value of these proteins in the pH regions where the levorotation and viscosity increase, since the exposure of a number of hydrophobic groups would increase the affinity of the protein for the top phase which contains a larger number of methyl groups. The fact that the protein molecules change configuration may also *per se* contribute to their preference for the top phase polymer, methylcellulose, which has a configuration different to that of the bottom phase polymer, dextran.

The K value of egg albumin also increases at a low pH but to a smaller degree than serum albumin. Egg albumin is considered to be more stable and compact at low pH values than serum albumin (29). However, this does not exclude the possibility that the surface of the egg albumin molecule has changed and become more hydrophobic at low pH values.

If the hypothesis that it is the increase in the number of hydrophobic groups on the exposed surface of the protein molecules which results in the increase of the K value, is correct, it means that partition in a polymer two-phase system would be a useful way of estimating the "hydrophobicity" of protein molecules. The ideal phase system for such a study would be a system produced by two polymers differing mainly in their non-polar groups and not in chain configuration, for example dextran and methyl dextran. Such a system has not yet been constructed, but should allow a more isolated study of the "hydrophobicity" than the dextran–methylcellulose system, the polymers of which differ considerably in chain configuration. It should be pointed out, however, that studies on the K value at different pH values are always difficult to interpret since different electrolytes are present and the binding of different ions varies differently with pH.

The results shown in Fig. 4.4 and Tables 4.7 and 4.8 show that the K values of virus particles and proteins at a neutral pH and in 0.15 M NaCl, depend mainly on the size of the particles and molecules. The fact that the points of Fig. 4.4 cluster around a line indicates that the constant λ of Brønsteds formula (eqn. 18 of Chapter 3) is not very different for the different substances partitioned, that is the particles and molecules behave as if their surface properties were rather similar. This may be naturally so, or because they have become so in the phase system by a firm adsorption on the particle surface of one of the polymers, for example dextran. Thus the acquired surface would be very similar for all particles. At present it is difficult to determine which is the more probable explanation.

The results of Fig. 4.4 and Tables 4.7 and 4.8 show that the dextran–methylcellulose system is not suitable for separation of particles with similar sizes since the K values for these are roughly the same; this also holds for small protein molecules. However, for the characterization and fractionation of large protein molecules of the size of the hemocyanins, and virus particles, this system is efficient. It may also be used for the estimation of at least the approximate size of certain particles such as viruses. By measuring the distribution of the infectivity, the size range to which the virus particles belong may be determined with the aid of the curve of Fig. 4.4. An advantage for practical work is that temperature variation has almost no influence on the distribution (Table 4.10). A disadvantage of the system is that its top phase is rather viscous and it requires a long time for phase separation.

The Distribution in the Dextran–Polyethylene Glycol System

The composition of the two phases of the dextran–polyethylene glycol system having a composition of 7 per cent (w/w) D 48 and 4.4 per cent (w/w) PEG 6000 at 20°C is found in Fig. 2.13. The bottom phase has a composition of 14.2 per cent (w/w) dextran and 0.9 per cent (w/w) polyethylene glycol while the top phase consists of 0.2 per cent (w/w) dextran and 7.7 per cent (w/w) polyethylene glycol. When salt is added to concentrations below 1 M, it is distributed equally between the phases (Fig. 2.25). Thus, as was also the case with the dextran–methylcellulose system, the two phases differ chemically only in the polymer composition and not in electrolyte content. However, the difference in composition of the two phases for the dextran–polyethylene glycol is greater than for the dextran–methylcellulose system. With proteins, it is thus possible to obtain partition coefficients which deviate more from unity in the dextran–polyethylene glycol than in the dextran–methylcellulose system.

The partition coefficient in the dextran–polyethylene glycol system depends on the size of the partitioned molecules and particles as in the dextran–methylcellulose system but in a less regular manner. Thus, no such relation between log K and surface area, as is shown in Fig. 4.4 for the dextran–methylcellulose system, is found for the dextran–polyethylene glycol system. Two proteins with similar molecular weights may thus go to different phases. The dextran–polyethylene glycol system is thus more specific and efficient for the fractionation of proteins in the molecular weight range 50 000–1 000 000 than is the dextran–methylcellulose system. Practical advantages of the dextran–polyethylene glycol system are the short settling time (5–30 minutes) and the lower viscosity of the top phase. In addition, since the composition of the system used is far removed from the critical point, it is not sensitive to changes in polymer composition or temperature.

The most striking characteristic of the dextran–polyethylene glycol system is the effect of electrolytes on the distribution. The fact that a substance may be transferred from one phase to the other simply by adding, for example, sodium chloride in excess of the sodium phosphate previously present (Fig. 4.15) or by replacing lithium by sodium ions (Fig. 4.15) is interesting from a theoretical point of view and also of great practical value.

The question arises as to the cause of this sensitivity to the electrolyte composition. It is assumed that, since the concentration of protein is low compared with the equivalent salt concentration, which is about equal in the two phases, Donnan effects are negligible, that is the potential difference between the two phases is zero; see Chapter 3. Thus, the K value is determined only by the activity coefficients of the protein in the two phases (eqn. (24) of Chapter 3). The activity coefficient of a protein in the different phases should therefore strongly depend on the electrolyte content. It was of interest to compare the solubility behaviour of proteins at different electrolyte compositions in the phase components dextran and polyethylene glycol. Although there is not necessarily a relation between the solubility of a solute in the phase components and its partition coefficient in the phase system, it is interesting to compare solubility with partition. For this purpose mixtures of polyethylene glycol and the proteins with different salt media were made up and the polymer concentration determined at which protein precipitation occurred. An experiment was made in which a protein solution was titrated with a concentrated polyethylene glycol solution with the same salt concentration until precipitation

154

| | % (w/w) PEG 6000 at start of precipitation | | |
Electrolyte composition	Serum albumin	Cerulo- plasmin	Phyco- erythrin
0.005 M KH$_2$PO$_4$ + 0.005 M K$_2$HPO$_4$	40	50	> 50
0.005 M KH$_2$PO$_4$ + 0.005 M K$_2$HPO$_4$ + 0.1 M KCl	22	12	> 50
0.05 M KH$_2$PO$_4$ + 0.05 M K$_2$HPO$_4$	50	27	> 50

occurred. This is reversible and by back titration with salt solution until the solution again becomes clear, it is possible to determine a fairly narrow interval of polyethylene glycol concentration in which precipitation begins.

The results are given in Table 4.17 and show that the proteins have very different solubilities in different salt media. Different proteins also behave differently; thus phycoerythrin is not precipitated in any salt media, while ceruloplasmin and serum albumin are. Phycoerythrin is the protein having the highest K value of these proteins, that is it has the greatest affinity for the polyethylene glycol phase. The solubility of serum albumin and ceruloplasmin in polyethylene glycol becomes less when KCl is added to the phosphate buffer, in analogy with the decrease in the K value when KCl is added to the phase system (Fig. 4.20). There is thus a qualitative agreement, for these proteins, between the partition behaviour in the phase system and the solubility behaviour in polyethylene glycol. A similar experiment on the solubility of proteins in dextran was not carried out since it is difficult to handle very concentrated, viscous dextran solutions.

In Chapter 2, it was mentioned that phase separation in mixtures of a polyelectrolyte (Na dextran sulfate or Na carboxymethylcellulose) and polyethylene glycol in water depends highly on the electrolyte content. Qualitatively, there is a striking similarity between the salt effect on these phase separations and the solubility behaviour of proteins in polyethylene glycol solutions.

When large amounts of salt are added to the dextran–polyethylene glycol system (Fig. 4.21) all proteins tend to partition in favour of the top phase. In the experiment of Fig. 4.21 there was a drop in the pH value with increasing NaCl concentration but a rather similar increase in the K value at higher NaCl concentrations is also obtained when the pH is kept constant. The increase in the K value is therefore mainly a direct effect of the increase in ionic strength. Even at high salt concentrations, NaCl distributes fairly equally between the two phases (Fig. 2.25). The activity coefficients (Eqn. (24) of Chapter 3) of the NaCl ions are therefore nearly the same in both phases. The greater affinity of the proteins for the top phase, which has less polar character than the bottom phase, with increasing salt concentration, may be a similar phenomenon to the increase in the solubility of amino acids and peptides in water–ethanol mixtures with increasing salt concentration (13), that is a "salting in" phenomenon.

The Adsorption at the Interface

Generally, in systems where adsorption at the interface is found, it occurs more frequently for larger particles such as whole cells and virus particles. In a given polymer–polymer system, adsorption at the interface is more likely the further the system is removed from the critical point. Both these results are qualitatively in agreement with the theoretical considerations of Chapter 3. Thus according to eqns. (20) and (21) of Chapter 3, adsorption at the interface should be greater the larger the size of the particles. The further a system from the critical point the greater its interfacial tension. Hence, from eqns. (20) and (21) of Chapter 3, there should be an increasing tendency to adsorption with increasing deviation from the critical composition.

Interfacial adsorption is more frequently met with the dextran-polyethylene glycol and the salt–polyethylene glycol systems, than with the dextran–methylcellulose system. Although no measurements of the interfacial tension of these systems have been made, it appears highly probable that the two former systems have larger interfacial tensions because of the much larger differences in composition of the phases. If this supposition is correct, it would explain why interfacial adsorption occurs more often in the dextran–polyethylene glycol and salt–polyethylene glycol systems. The interfacial tension of low molecular weight phase systems is larger than that of polymer phase systems and, in the author's experience, collection of particles at the interface occurs very frequently in low molecular weight phase systems.

However, the fact that a substance collects at the interface does not necessarily mean that its particles or molecules are adsorbed there according to the mechanism outlined in Chapter 3, Fig. 3.1 and 3.2, that is each single particle has a lower potential energy at the interface. The collection of a substance at the interface may be the result of a precipitation of the substance with the formation of a third phase which simply separates by virtue of a density difference and collects between the two phases. We may also suppose that a combination of these two mechanisms may operate.

A study of the behaviour of a substance in the two individual phases, that is when no interface is present, is a convenient way of distinguishing between these two mechanisms. Thus if there is no sign of precipitation or aggregation when the particles are suspended in each phase separately, but they collect at the interface when the two phases are mixed, this indicates that adsorption at the interface may take place according to the principles of Figs. 3.1 and 3.2. The distribution of *Chlorella* in the dextran–polyethylene glycol system is an example.

Alternatively, if precipitation takes place even when the phases are separated and no significant further change in the concentration of solute takes place after the two phases are mixed, this indicates that the substance between the two phases consists of a third phase. An example is the distribution of *Helix pomatia* hemocyanin in the dextran–polyethylene glycol system in 0.1 M NaCl and 0.01 M phosphate buffer, pH $= 6$.

That two fundamentally different mechanisms underlie the congregation of particles at the interface in the two cases of *Chlorella* and hemocyanin is shown by the different concentration dependence. Whereas with *Chlorella* there is a linear relation between the concentration of particles suspended in the top phase and the amount of particles adsorbed at the interface up to very large concentrations of cells (linear adsorption isotherm), in the case of hemocyanin the concentration in the top phase is almost constant when different amounts of hemocyanin are added above a certain concentration. The latter case is to be expected if the top phase is in equilibrium with a precipitated hemocyanin phase.

Concluding Remarks

It has been shown in this chapter that high molecular weight sub-stances such as proteins and viruses can be partitioned in a polymer two-phase system such that a reproducible partition coefficient can be measured. The partition coefficient is, in most cases studied so far, independent of the solute concentration and the presence of other solutes. The value of the partition coefficient may thus be used for the characterisation of biological macromolecules.

A prerequisite for such a characterization is a carefully specified phase system with fairly well defined polymer fractions. The electro-lyte composition must also be controlled and particularly with the dextran–polyethylene glycol system and with all systems containing a polyelectrolyte. An important result of this investigation is that influences of minor quantities of certain electrolytes are almost entirely eliminated when an excess of neutral salt is added. For the characterization of, for example, a protein by its partition coefficient, it is therefore suggested that the partition be determined in a suitable buffer with an excess of, for example, NaCl or KCl. Systems very near the critical point should, if possible be avoided, since these re-quire much more experimental control to get reproducible results.

Most of the quantitative experiments on the influence of electrolytes have been carried out with proteins since they give finite partition coefficients which can easily be measured. Quantitative studies on the distribution of larger particles, such as whole cells, between a phase and the interface are not so easy to carry out. However, the results obtained with proteins may be used at least as a guide for the construction of suitable phase systems for particles.

REFERENCES

1. ADAMS, M. H., *J. Gen. Physiol.*, *31*, 417 (1948).
2. ALBERTSSON, P. Å., *Biochim. et Biophys. Acta*, *27*, 378 (1958).
3. — *Nature*, *182*, 709 (1958).
4. ALBERTSSON, P. Å., and FRICK, G., *Biochim. et Biophys. Acta*, *37*, 230 (1960).
5. ALBERTSSON, P. Å., and NYNS, ED. J., *Nature*, *184*, 1465 (1959).
6. — *Arkiv Kemi* (1960), in press.
7. BOEDTKER, H., and SIMMONS, N. S., *J. Am. Chem. Soc.*, *80*, 2550 (1958).
8. BRAY, R. C., personal communication.

9. BROHULT, S., *Nova Acta Soc. Scient. Upsaliensis*, *12*, No. 4 (1940).

10. BROSTEAUX, J., and ERIKSSON-QUENSEL, I. B., *Arch. Phys. biol.*, *12*, No. 4 (1935).

11. BRØNSTED, J. N., *Z. phys. Chem.*, A. (Bodenstein-Festband), 2571, 1931.

12. BRØNSTED, J. N., and WARMING, E., *Z. phys. Chem.*, *A 155*, 343 (1931).

13. EDSALL, I. T., and WYMAN, J., Biophysical chemistry, Academic Press, New York, 1958.

14. ERIKSSON-QUENSEL, I. B., *Biochem. J.*, *32*, 585 (1938).

15. FISCHER, R., *Experientia*, *3*, 29 (1947).

16. FOSTER, J. F., *in* PUTNAM, F. W., The Plasma Proteins, Vol. 1, p. 179 (1960).

17. FRICK, G., and ALBERTSSON, P. Å., *Nature*, *183*, 1070 (1959).

18. HANZON, V., and PHILIPSON, L., *J. Ultrastructure Res.*, *3*, 420 (1960).

19. HARDT, C. R., HUDDLESON, I. F., and BALL, C. D., *Science*, *98*, 309 (1943).

20. HEIRWEGH, K., BORIGNON, H., and LONTIE, R., *Arch. Intern. Physiol. et Biochemie*, *67*, 514 (1959).

21. KIERMEIER, F., and KÖBERLEIN, W., *Bioch. Z.*, *329*, 247 (1957).

22. LIF, T., FRICK, G., and ALBERTSSON, P. Å., to be published.

23. NORRBY, E., and ALBERTSSSON, P. Å., *Nature*, in press.

24. PHILIPSON, L., ALBERTSSON, P. Å., and FRICK, G., *Virology*, *11*, 553 (1960).

25. SCHAFFER, F. L., and SCHWERDT, C. E., *Advances Virus Res.*, *6*, 170 (1959).

26. SCHRAMM, G., and BERGER, G., *Z. Naturforsch.*, *7 b*, 284 (1952).

27. STERMAN, M. D., and FOSTER, J. F., *J. Am. Chem. Soc.*, *78*, 3652, (1956).

28. SVEDBERG, T., and PEDERSEN, K., The Ultracentrifuge, Oxford University Press, London, New York, 1940.

29. TANFORD, C., *in* Symposium on Protein Structure, p. 35, ed. A. NEUBERGER, Methuen & Co., Ltd, London; J. Wiley & Sons, Inc., New York, 1958.

30. TAVEL, P. v., *Helv. Chim. Acta*, *38*, 520 (1955).

31. WESSLÉN, T., ALBERTSSON, P. Å., and PHILIPSON, L., *Arch. ges. Virusforsch.*, *9*, 510 (1959).

32. WILLIAMS, R. C., *Advances Virus Res.*, *2*, 183 (1954).

33. WILLIAMS, R. C., and FRASER, P. J., *J. Bacteriol.*, *66*, 458 (1953).

34. YANG, J. T., and FOSTER, J. F., *J. Am. Chem. Soc.*, *76*, 1588 (1954).

5. Countercurrent Distribution

INTRODUCTION

The principle of the method of countercurrent distribution is well known and has been treated in a number of books and review articles of which those of Craig & Craig (7), Craig (8), Hecker (12), Rauen & Stamm (22), and Tavel & Signer (24) may be mentioned.

By this method, a large number of extraction steps are carried out in order to separate substances having different partition coefficients. Thus, if two substances are only slightly separated by one distribution in a separation funnel, they may be almost completely separated after several distributions in an automatic apparatus. In the diagram obtained by the countercurrent distribution technique each substance gives rise to one peak; the position and form of this peak is determined by the partition coefficient of the solute, the phase volume ratio, and the number of distribution steps. It is possible to calculate the theoretical curve, according to which a single substance will distribute, provided it behaves ideally. A comparison of the experimental curve with the theoretical curve then allows important conclusions as to whether the distributed substance is pure or behaves non-ideally. Countercurrent distribution serves therefore as an important analytical tool, but, since different substances are separated from each other, it may also be used for preparative purposes.

Disadvantages of the method are that a special apparatus has to be constructed, and for many distributions it becomes rather laborious. However, with the fully automatic countercurrent apparatus now available commercially an experiment requires little manual work, the main work being devoted to the choice of the right solvent system.

An outstanding feature of countercurrent distribution is that it is based upon several steps each involving an equilibrium between two liquid phases. As mentioned in Chapter 1, this is particularly advantageous when macromolecules are involved, since for these it is thought to be easier to achieve an equilibrium between two liquid phases

160

than between a liquid and a solid phase. To develop suitable solvents, which may be applied to the characterization and fractionation of macromolecules such as proteins, nucleic acids and viruses in a counter-current apparatus, is therefore of the greatest importance.

So far, mainly low molecular substances such as vitamins and hormones have been studied by countercurrent distribution, but a number of larger polypeptides and small proteins have also been successfully distributed. These include insulin (10), adrenocortico-tropins, growth hormone, lactogenic hormone (21), lysozyme (6, 16), ribonuclease (16), casein (9, 24, 26), serum albumin (11, 17, 18), and hemoglobin (13).

Ribonucleic acid has also been fractionated by countercurrent distribution (14, 15, 19, 20, 27). A few synthetic polymers such as polyglycols (2, 23) and cellulose acetate (3) have been distributed in low molecular weight phase systems but only the lower molecular parts of the latter polymer could be partitioned between the phases.

Many difficulties present themselves, as was discussed in Chapter 1, when carrying out liquid–liquid extractions of proteins in low molecular solvents. Due to their large molecular size they usually distribute rather unilaterally, giving rise to partition coefficients which are either very small or very large; for a countercurrent experiment the partition coefficients should be in the range 0.1–10. There is also always a risk of denaturation which may be caused by the interfaces and the or-ganic solvents of the phase system. In some cases these difficulties have been overcome by working either very near the critical compo-siton (24) or by introducing complexing agents such as trichloroacetic acid (11). The effect of the latter is to stabilize the protein against denaturation and to make it more soluble in the organic phase.

However, most of the difficulties mentioned above can be avoided, even for very large protein molecules, by using aqueous polymer phase systems, and in this chapter, a number of countercurrent distribution experiments with such phase systems will be described.

Two types of distribution have been used (Fig. 5.1).

The first, Fig. 5.1a, involves the distribution of the substance be-tween the two phases, no significant adsorption of the solute taking place at the interface. This is the conventional way of distribution in a countercurrent experiment and will be referred to as *liquid–liquid countercurrent distribution*. Each substance is characterized by its

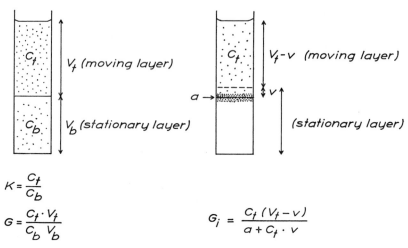

Fig. 5.1. The difference between the distribution type in liquid–liquid countercurrent distribution (*a*), and liquid–interfacial countercurrent distribution (*b*). To the left, no significant adsorption at the interface takes place. The whole top phase is the moving layer in the countercurrent apparatus. To the right, the distribution takes place between the top phase and the interface. The bottom phase, the interface and a small layer above the interface together form the stationary layer in the countercurrent apparatus.

partition coefficient, K, and is transported along the distribution train according to its distribution ratio, G, which is the ratio between the *amount* of substance in the top phase and the bottom phase i.e.

$$G = \frac{C_t \cdot V_t}{C_b \cdot V_b} = K \cdot L, \qquad (1)$$

where C_t, C_b, V_t and V_b are the concentrations and volumes of the top and bottom phases respectively and L is the volume ratio.

The other distribution type (Fig. 5.1*b*), which will be called *liquid–interface countercurrent distribution*, involves the distribution of the solute between one of the phases and the interface. This is used mainly for larger particles. In, for example, Fig. 5.1*b* the distribution takes place between the upper phase and the interface. The bottom phase, together with the interface and a small layer of the top phase just above the interface, is kept stationary in the apparatus while the rest of the top phase is the moving phase. Let the volume of the top phase be V_t, the volume of the layer of the top phase which is kept stationary in the distribution train be v, and C_t be the concentration of the solute in the top phase, and a the amount of the solute adsorbed at the interface. The ratio which is of interest for the countercurrent distribution is then

$$G_i = \frac{(V_t - v)\,C_t}{v \cdot C_t + a}. \tag{2}$$

When the substance behaves ideally, i.e. the adsorption at the interface is reversible and proportional to C_t, it will be transported along the distribution train according to the G_i value and, for calculation of theoretical curves, this may be used in the same way as the G value in liquid–liquid countercurrent distribution.

In a similar manner a distribution between the bottom phase and the interface may be used for countercurrent distribution. The top phase, together with the interface and a small layer below it, is then the moving layer in the countercurrent experiment while the remaining bottom phase is stationary.

LIQUID–LIQUID COUNTERCURRENT DISTRIBUTION

A system which has been found useful for countercurrent distribution experiments with proteins is the dextran–polyethylene glycol system D48–PEG6000 (see Figs. 2.13 and 2.14). It has the advantage of a comparatively short settling time (15–30 minutes) and the top phase, which is the moving phase, has a comparatively low viscosity. As was shown in the previous chapter, the partition coefficient of a protein depends on the ionic composition and thus by suitable additions of salt a K value convenient for a countercurrent distribution may be obtained.

The standard phase system used contains 7 per cent (w/w) D48 and 4.4 per cent (w/w) PEG6000 in water. 1 kg of this system has a volume of 976 ml. The phase system is prepared in two different ways depending on the amount of salt added.

1. *Salt concentrations up to 1 mole per kg of standard phase system.* Each ml of water of the standard phase sytem is replaced by 1 ml

of the added salt solution. As an example, the mixtures prepared for the experiments shown in Figs. 5.2, 5.3, and 5.4 are given below.

Mixture for the experiments in Figs. 5.2 and 5.3.

20% (w/w) D 48	350 g
30% (w/w) PEG 6000	146.67 g
0.05 M KH$_2$PO$_4$	100 ml
0.05 M K$_2$HPO$_4$	100 ml
0.22 M KCl	100 ml
H$_2$O	203.33 g

Mixture for the experiment in Fig. 5.4.

20% (w/w) D 48	350 g
30% (w/w) PEG 6000	146.67 g
0.05 M KH$_2$PO$_4$	100 ml
0.05 M K$_2$HPO$_4$	100 ml
5 M KCl	150 ml
H$_2$O	153.33 g

2. *Salt concentrations above 1 mole per kg of phase system.* In this case the salt is added dry to the standard phase system. As an example, the mixture used for the experiments in Figs. 5.5 and 5.6 is given below.

Mixture for the experiments of Figs. 5.5 and 5.6.

20% (w/w) D 48	350 g
30% (w/w) PEG 6000	146.67 g
0.05 M NaH$_2$PO$_4$	100 ml
0.05 M Na$_2$HPO$_4$	100 ml
H$_2$O	403.33 g
NaCl	146.15 g (2.5 moles)

The composition of the two phases of this mixture may be found in Figs. 2.24 and 2.25. The PEG 6000 is usually purified by precipitation with ether from an acetone solution (see Chapter 1).

Protein is always added to the first tube in the form of a solution and a special mixture is therefore prepared for the first tube in such a way that each ml of protein solution replaces 1 ml of water.

It should be pointed out that when large amounts of NaCl are added to a solution containing 0.01 M Na phosphate (equimolar concentra-

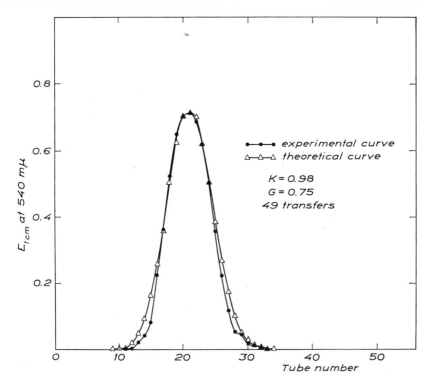

Fig. 5.2. Countercurrent distribution of phycoerythrin (an algal protein with a molecular weight of about 290000) in the dextran–polyethylene glycol system. The system contained 0.005 moles KH_2PO_4, 0.005 moles K_2HPO_4 and 0.022 moles KCl per 976 ml of the phase system. (976 ml is the volume of 1 kg of the standard phase system used for countercurrent experiment; it has a composition of 7 % (w/w) D 48 and 4.4 % PEG 6000.) The first tube was charged with 28.2 mg protein. Extinction was measured for samples from the bottom phase diluted with an equal weight of water. The K value was determined experimentally. The G value was calculated from the maximum position of the curve. The theoretical curve was adjusted to the maximum point. From ref. (1).

tions of NaH_2PO_4 and Na_2HPO_4) the pH value drops considerably and in order to have neutral pH another buffer system should be used.

The number of inversions has varied between 25 and 50. All experiments described below have been carried out at room temperature.

Figs. 5.2 and 5.3 show the distribution of purified preparations of phycoerythrin and phycocyanin respectively. The experiments were carried out in an automatic apparatus constructed similarly to the Craig all-glass apparatus (7, 12). As can be seen, the experimental curves adhere well to the theoretically calculated ones with only a

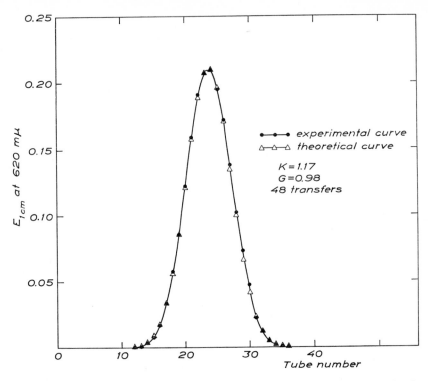

Fig. 5.3. Countercurrent distribution of phycocyanin (an algal protein with a molecular weight of about 150000 at pH = 7) in the same system as in Fig. 5.2. The first tube was charged with 7 ml of a solution of phycocyanin with an extinction of 20.3 when measured at 620 mμ in a 1-cm cell. The K and G values were obtained as in Fig. 2. From ref. (1).

slight narrowing of the phycoerythrin peak being observed. In both experiments a salt composition was selected which gave a K value around 1; this was done with the aid of the curves in Fig. 4.20.

In Fig. 5.4 an experiment is shown in which an artificial mixture of the two proteins is separated by countercurrent distribution. Here a salt composition was also selected from Fig. 4.20, which gave a large enough separation factor. In this experiment phycocyanin behaves ideally which is seen from both the adherence of the theoretical and experimental curves and from the constant K value determined experimentally for tubes no. 32–43. The experimental curve of phyco-erythrin deviates from the theoretical curve considerably and the experimentally determined K values also vary for the different tubes. Whether this behaviour is due to a heterogeneity of the protein or to a

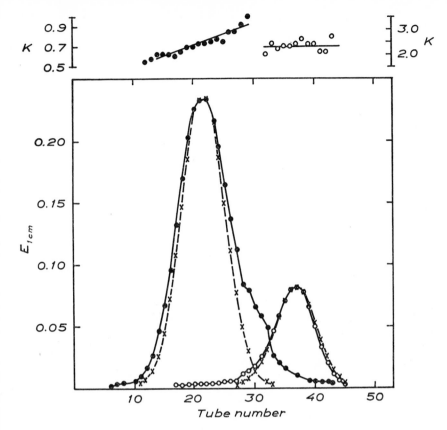

Fig. 5.4. Separation of a mixture of phycoerythrin and phycocyanin in a dextran–polyethylene glycol system containing 0.005 mole KH_2PO_4, 0.005 mole K_2HPO_4, and 0.75 mole KCl per 976 ml of the phase system (see Fig. 5.2.). The protein mixture was put into the first two tubes. The extinctions given are those of the top phase. The K values plotted above have been determined experimentally. The estimation of protein in the two phases was done by determination of extinction of the diluted phases at 495 mμ for phycoerythrin and 620 mμ for phycocyanin. Each theoretical curve is the sum of two theoretical curves calculated from their respective starting points. 53 transfers. From ref. (1).

gradual transformation during the run, is difficult to say from this single experiment. Heterogeneity of phycoerythrin has been demonstrated by calcium phosphate chromatography (25).

In Figs. 5.5 and 5.6, experiments with an enzyme, ceruloplasmin, a copper containing oxidase from human serum, is shown. In Fig. 5.5 an almost pure product was tested. As may be seen, the activity curve adheres closely to the theoretical curve while the protein

167

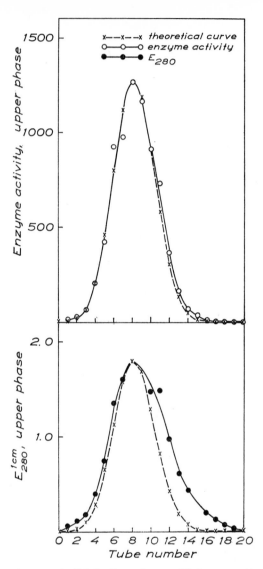

Fig. 5.5. Countercurrent distribution of a purified preparation of ceruloplasmin.

curve (extinction at 280 mμ) indicates that impurities are present which have higher K values. This experiment clearly demonstrates the usefulness of countercurrent distribution as a test on purity of an enzyme preparation.

An experiment (5) with ceruloplasmin from human serum, partially purified by calcium phosphate chromatography (4), is shown in Fig.

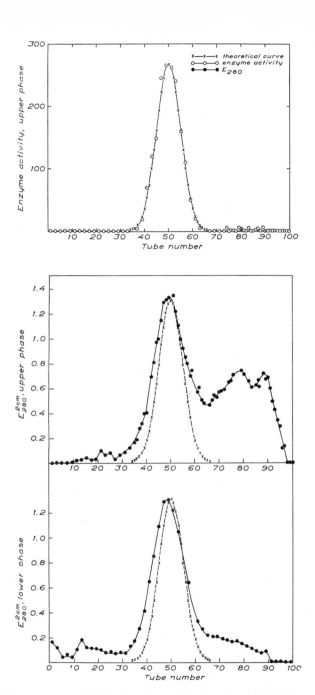

Fig. 5.6. Countercurrent distribution of a preparation of ceruloplasmin, partly purified by calcium phosphate chromatography. Figure at the top shows the enzyme activity curve together with the theoretical curve calculated from a G value of 1.0. Figures in the middle and at the bottom show the protein curves of the upper and lower phases respectively and theoretical curves calculated from the same G value as above (5).

5.6. This product contains considerable amounts of other serum components and to obtain an efficient separation of the enzyme, NaCl was added to a concentration of 2.5 moles per kg of the standard phase system. As judged from Fig. 4.21, this gives a K value of about 1 for ceruloplasmin; most of the other components will have K values differing from 1, either lower or higher, and will therefore be separated from the enzyme. As may be seen in Fig. 5.6, the enzyme activity curve is almost identical with the theoretical one and the enzyme thus distributes ideally even in the presence of large amounts of other proteins.

Discussion

The experiments described above, together with other as yet unpublished experiments (5), show that in most cases the distribution of a protein in the dextran–polyethylene glycol system follows the Nernst distribution law, that is the K value is independent of the concentration of the partitioned substance and the presence of impurities. This ideal behaviour seems to hold even at high protein concentrations. In the experiment of Fig. 5.6, the first tube, containing 10 ml of each phase, was thus charged with about 2 g protein and the enzyme still distributed ideally. As was shown in Fig. 4.24, the K value of serum albumin is constant up to concentrations of about 10 per cent.

It is fairly simple to select a suitable K value by determination of the K value for a few systems with varying amounts of salt, for example, in the presence of 0.01 M phosphate buffer alone and with increasing amounts of NaCl such as illustrated by Fig. 4.21. It appears (see Fig. 4.21) that the separation factor increases with increasing salt concentration. When an experiment is run at room temperature, it is an advantage to have high salt concentration since it prevents bacterial growth. It should be pointed out that the settling time is 15–30 minutes for this phase system only when the upper phase is equal to or larger than the lower phase; this is usually the case in countercurrent experiments.

The most accurate results are obtained when a protein is estimated by light absorption or its enzyme activity. If it is to be measured at 280 mμ, polyethylene–glycol which has been purified by precipitation (see Chapter 1) is used. The phases are first diluted and cleared by centrifugation if they appear turbid. Unfortunately the method for protein determination according to Lowry *et al.* cannot be applied when the protein concentration is low in the phases. The biuret method may be applied to the top phase. Nitrogen determination according to the Kjeldahl method can be applied to both phases.

Recovery of the proteins

When an experiment is completed, it is desirable to recover the polymer-free protein. This may be done in a number of different ways, the most suitable depending on the properties and the amount of the actual protein. A few examples which have been tested will now be described.

1. *Adsorption of the protein.* By this method, the protein is adsorbed on a column which does not adsorb the polymers; hence the latter may be washed away followed by elution of the protein. This has been applied to the recovery of phycoerythrin and ceruloplasmin used in the experiments described above. The proteins were adsorbed on a calcium phosphate column (25). The polymers do not influence the adsorption; they only reduce the time of flow. In the case of ceruloplasmin the tubes numbered 40–60 in Fig. 5.6 were combined and NaCl added up to about 5 M. The protein was then transferred to the top phase (see Fig. 4.21). This was then dialysed against 0.125 M sodium phosphate buffer pH 6.8 and added to a calcium phosphate column whereby the ceruloplasmin was adsorbed. After washing the column, the enzyme was eluted with 0.5 M buffer.

2. *Transfer of the protein to a phase from which it can be precipitated.* When high ammonium sulfate or potassium phosphate concentrations are added to a dextran–polyethylene glycol system the dextran phase will be completely free of polyethylene glycol. A protein in the dextran phase may then be precipitated out with ammonium sulfate.

In the dextran–methylcellulose system, the methylcellulose is precipitated out at about 10% ammonium sulfate; the remaining protein may then be precipitated by increasing the ammonium sulfate concentration. This can be used for the recovery of phycoerythrin from the dextran–methylcellulose system in the following way.

Ammonium sulfate is added to 10 per cent (w/w), the methylcellulose precipitate filtered off, and the phycoerythrin precipitated by 20 per cent (w/w) ammonium sulfate.

3. *Transfer of the protein to a polymer-free phase.* As may be seen in Fig. 4.21, a number of proteins are transferred to the top phase of the dextran–polyethylene glycol system when a high concentration of NaCl is present. This top phase contains polyethylene glycol as the only polymer. Polyethylene glycol forms a phase system with ammonium sulfate or potassium phosphate, the bottom phase of which contains almost only salt (see Figs. 2.40 and 2.41). If a protein is transferred to this salt phase we have separated it from the polymers. An example of such a procedure now follows.

Fractions, containing upper and lower phase, from a countercurrent distribution experiment with ceruloplasmin (the same phase system as in Fig. 5.6) were combined and NaCl added up to 5 M. A phase system similar to no. 7 of Fig. 2.24 is obtained. The top phase contains most of the enzyme and about 8.5 per cent (w/w) polyethylene glycol but no dextran. In Fig. 5.7. the top phase is represented by point a. It is dialyzed to remove the major part of the NaCl and then added to PEG 6000 and potassium phosphate (equimolar parts of KH_2PO_4 and K_2HPO_4) in such proportions that a system containing 24 per cent (w/w) PEG 6000 and 6 per cent potassium phosphate is obtained (system B in Fig. 5.7). The enzyme is thereby transferred to the bottom phase represented by point b in Fig. 5.7 and containing almost no polyethylene glycol.

In the procedures described above the proteins are concentrated (10–100 times) as a result of their recovery. This is an advantage since after a countercurrent distribution the protein has been diluted due to spreading over a number of tubes. To concentrate the protein after a run is therefore often a desirable step prior to further purification or analysis.

LIQUID–INTERFACE COUNTERCURRENT DISTRIBUTION

An experiment with the unicellular algae *Chlorella pyrenoidosa* is shown in Fig. 5.8. The experiment was carried out manually, the top phases being transferred by a pipette. Each tube contained 2.45 ml

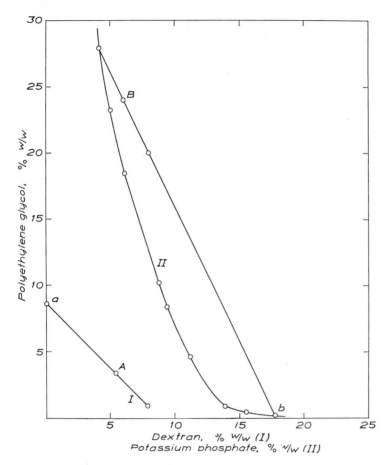

Fig. 5.7. Parts of the phase diagrams of the dextran–polyethylene glycol system (D 48–PEG 6000; system no. 7 of Fig. 2.24) and potassium phosphate–polyethylene glycol system (Fig. 2.40) used for the transfer of a protein into a polymer-free phase. The enzyme is first partitioned in system B, in which most of the enzyme activity is found in the top phase represented by point *a*. This top phase is collected and PEG 6000 and potassium phosphate are added to give a new phase system represented by point *B*. In this system the enzyme is transferred to the bottom phase represented by point *b* and containing practically no polyethylene glycol.

bottom phase and 2.4 ml top phase; 2 ml of the top phase was transferred. In the formula above, v is therefore 0.4 ml. After the experiment was finished, the concentration (C_t) of cells was determined in each top phase and the total amount in each tube. The amount of cells present at the interface (a) was then calculated. As may be seen in Fig. 5.8, a major part of the *Chlorella* is suspended in the top

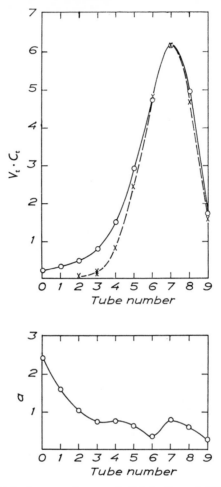

Fig. 5.8. Liquid–interface countercurrent distribution of *Chlorella pyrenoidosa* in a dextran–polyethylene glycol system containing 7 % (w/w) D 48, 4.4 % (w/w) PEG 6000, 0.005 M KH$_2$PO$_4$, 0.005 M K$_2$HPO$_4$, and 0.03 M KCl. Temperature: 20°C.

phase and gives rise to a peak in the diagram at tube no. 7, corresponding to a G_i value of 3. For tubes no. 5–9 the experimental points agree well with the theoretical points. For the other tubes the curve shows a tailing. The remaining cells are present at the interface and in the first tubes almost all cells are attached to the interface. The top phase of the tubes no. 5–9 were combined, and the cells recovered by repeated low speed centrifugation to wash away the polymers. The same was done with the cells at the interface of tubes

174

no. 0–2. The two preparations were then distributed in a phase system having the same composition as that used in the countercurrent experiment. The following result was obtained.

All cells of tubes no. 0–2 collected at the interface, which is in agreement with their behaviour in the countercurrent experiment.

About 50 per cent of the cells from tubes no. 5–9 collected at the interface while the remaining cells were suspended in the top phase. According to their behaviour in the countercurrent experiment only about 14 per cent should collect at the interface. It is difficult to explain this disagreement but it might be due to an aggregation of the cells caused by the centrifugation used for their recovery.

However, the fact that the cells of tubes 0–2 and 5–7 distribute differently both in the countercurrent experiment and after they have been recovered is an indication that the two preparations are really different.

Liquid–interface countercurrent distribution has recently also been carried out on various nucleic acid preparations including DNA from phage T2 and calf thymus, and RNA from liver microsomes. It has been found that fractionation may be obtained in the phase systems NaDS 68–MC 4000 in 0.3 M NACl (see Table 4.15) and NaDS 68–PEG 6000 in 0.3 M NaCl, see ref. (22) of Chapter 4.

REFERENCES

1. ALBERTSSON, P. Å., and NYNS, ED. J., *Nature, 184,* 1465 (1959).
2. ALMIN, K. E., *Acta Chem. Scand., 13,* 1278 (1959).
3. — *Svensk Papperstidning,* 62, 594 (1959).
4. BROMAN, L., *Nature, 182,* 1655 (1958).
5. BROMAN, L., and ALBERTSSON, P. Å., to be published.
6. CRAENHALS, E., and LEONIS, J., *Bull. soc. chim. Belges, 64,* 58 (1955).
7. CRAIG, L. C., and CRAIG, D., *in* Technique of Organic Chemistry, edited by A. WEISSBERGER, Vol. III, Part 1, second edition, Intersicence Publishers Inc., New York, 1956.
8. CRAIG, L. C., *in* A Laboratory Manual of Analytical Methods of Protein Chemistry, edited by P. ALEXANDER and R. J. BLOCK, Vol. I, p. 121, Pergamon Press, Oxford, 1960.
9. ELLFOLK, N., *Acta Chem. Scand., 11,* 1317 (1957).
10. HARFENIST, E. J., and CRAIG, L. C., *J. Am. Chem. Soc., 74,* 3083 (1952).
11. HAUSMANN, W., and CRAIG, L. C., *J. Am. Chem. Soc., 80,* 2703 (1958).

12. HECKER, E., Verteilungsverfahren im Laboratorium, Monographien zu *Angewandte Chemie* und *Chemie-Ingenieur-Technik*, No. 67, Verlag Chemie, GMBH, Weinheim/Bergstr., Germany, 1955.

13. HILL, R. J. and CRAIG, L. C., *J. Am. Chem. Soc.*, *81*, 2272 (1959).

14. HOLLEY, R. W. and MERRIL, S. H., *J. Am. Chem. Soc. 81*, 753 (1959).

15. HOLLEY, R. W., DOCTOR, B. P., MERRIL, S. H., and FAVIDA, M. S., *Biochim. et Biophys. Acta, 35*, 272 (1959).

16. KING, T. P., and CRAIG, L. C., *J. Am. Chem. Soc., 80*, 3366 (1958).

17. KING, T. P., YPHANTIS, D. A., and CRAIG, L. C., *J. Am. Chem. Soc., 82*, 3350 (1960).

18. KING, T. P., YPHANTIS, D. A., and CRAIG, L. C., *J. Am. Chem. Soc., 82*, 3355 (1960).

19. KIRBY, K. S., *Trans. Faraday Soc., 55*, 490 (1959).

20. KIRBY, K. S., *Biochim. et Biophys. Acta, 41*, 338 (1960).

21. LI, C. H., *Advances in Protein Chem., 11*, 101 (1956).

22. RAUEN, H. M., and STAMM, W., Gegenstromverteilung, Anleitungen für die chemische Laboratoriumspraxis, Vol. VI, Springer-Verlag, Berlin, Göttingen, Heidelberg, 1953.

23. SCHULZ, C. V., and NORDT, E. J., *J. prakt. Chem., 155*, 115 (1940).

24. TAVEL, P. v., and SIGNER, R., *Advances in Protein Chem., 11*, 237 (1956).

25. TISELIUS, A., HJERTÉN, S., and LEVIN, Ö., *Arch. Biochem. and Biophys., 65*, 132 (1956).

26. WALTER, J. O., Dissertation, Berne, 1952.

27. WARNER, R. C., and VAIMBERG, P., *Fed. Proc., 17*, 331 (1958).

6. Isolation of Ribonucleoprotein Particles from Rat Brain Microsomes (1)

Microsomes from different tissues consist essentially of two sub-microscopic structures; vesicles formed by fragments of the cyto-plasmic membranes ("the endoplasmic reticulum" or "α cytomem-branes"), and small particles often attached to these membranes (6, 7, 8, 9). In order to study their biochemical properties the separation of these two structures has previously been attempted by various physical and chemical methods (6). Thus the vesicles contain mainly protein and lipids and the particles are composed of ribonucleoprotein. These particles are often called ribosomes or ribonucleoprotein par-ticles and have received much attention because of their role in protein synthesis (4). Ribonucleoprotein particles have also been isolated from a number of micro-organisms such as yeast, bacteria, and algae and from plant cells (4).

Fractionation of rat brain microsomes by various centrifugation techniques has been carried out by Toschi (10). When differential centrifugation was applied, it was found that the ribonucleoprotein particles were always contaminated by comparatively large vesicles. This may be explained in the following way. In a suitable salt medium the ribonucleoprotein particles are relatively uniform in size while the vesicles vary considerably in size and form as is schematically depicted in Fig. 6.1. The vesicles have a lower density than the ribo-nucleoprotein particles and the latter therefore sediment faster than vesicles of the same size. However, vesicles larger than the ribonucleo-protein particles will approach these in sedimentation behaviour. Thus the vesicles and the ribonucleoprotein particles lying between the broken lines of Fig. 6.1 will not be separated by differential centri-fugation.

As was shown in Chapter 4, the distribution of particles in the dextran–methylcellulose system is mainly determined by the surface area of the particles. If this also holds for microsomes, ribonucleo-

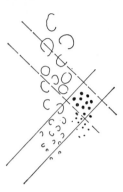

Fig. 6.1. A hypothetical figure showing the different kinds of separation obtained by differential centrifugation and partition in the dextran–methylcellulose system. The points symbolize ribonucleoprotein particles and the sketched curves symbolize vesicles from a microsome preparation. Particles and vesicles lying between the two broken lines have approximately the same sedimentation behavior in differential centrifugation due to the combined effect of the larger size but lower density of the vesicles. The vesicles lying between the two continuous lines have the same surface area as the ribonucleoprotein particles and would therefore behave similarly in the dextran–methylcellulose system if the surface area is the only determining factor for the partition coefficient.

protein particles and vesicles of the same surface area, i.e. those between the continuous lines of Fig. 6.1, should have similar K values. However, these K values would differ from those of the large vesicles sedimenting together with the ribonucleoprotein particles. A combination of sedimentation and partition should therefore allow a better purification than either of the two methods separately.

This was the basis for the following method for the isolation of ribonucleoprotein particles from rat brain microsomes (1). The microsomes are first distributed in the dextran methylcellulose system A1 (see Fig. 6.2), identical with that described in Chapter 2, Fig. 2.27, and used for the distribution of proteins and virus particles (see Tables 4.7 and 4.8). In this system both the ribonucleoprotein particles and the vesicles partition in favour of the bottom phase (see Fig. 6.3). The ribonucleoprotein particles have K values in the range of 0.2–0.4 while the vesicles have much smaller values. The top phase (represented by point a in Fig. 6.2) will therefore contain mostly ribonucleoprotein particles and no vesicles. Since the volume of the top phase is larger than the bottom, a considerable part of the ribonucleoprotein particles free of vesicles will be present in the top phase.

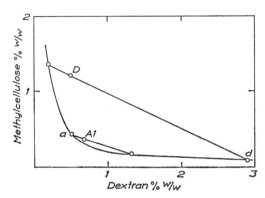

Fig. 6.2 Part of the phase diagram of the dextran–methylcellulose system D 68–MC 4000 at 4°C. The microsome preparation is first distributed in system A1. The top phase, represented by point a, contains a large part of purified ribonucleoprotein particles. By adding polymers to this phase, a new system D is obtained and the ribonucleoprotein particles are then concentrated into the small bottom phase, represented by point d.

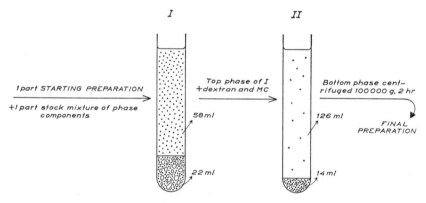

Fig. 6.3. A scheme for the fractionation of rat brain microsomes in two-phase systems of dextran and methylcellulose. Particles and vesicles are symbolized. From ref. (1).

Soluble constituents, such as proteins, have K values of nearly 1 and a large proportion of these will also be present in the top phase. After the top phase has been removed, fresh top phase is added to the bottom phase, the above procedure repeated, and more ribonucleoprotein particles transferred to the top phase. The top phases thus obtained are combined and suitable amounts of dextran and methylcellulose are added so that a new phase system with a small bottom phase is obtained (see tube II of Fig. 6.3). This system is represented by point D in Fig. 6.2 and is further removed from the critical point

179

than system A1. The ribonucleoprotein particles have a much lower K value in this system and they will therefore be concentrated in the small bottom phase (represented by point d in Fig. 6.2); soluble constituents are not concentrated to the same extent since they have K values in the range of 0.5–1. The ribonucleoprotein particles are finally removed from the bottom phase of tube II by high speed centrifugation.

The phase systems also contained 0.25 M sucrose, 0.001 M MgCl$_2$ and K$_2$HPO$_4$ to preserve the microsomal structures. Phase separation was speeded up by centrifugation. The experimental technique was as follows.

A stock mixture was prepared by weighing into a flask 13.6 g of a 10 per cent (w/w) solution of D68, 72 g of a 1 per cent (w/w) solution of MC4000, 0.5 g 0.2 M MgCl$_2$, 0.5 g 0.2 M K$_2$HPO$_4$, and 13.4 g H$_2$O, i.e. a total of 100 g. This stock mixture gives, when later diluted 1:1 with the microsome preparation, the desired phase system. After the contents of the flask had been mixed by gentle shaking, a sample was immediately removed using a pipette with a wide orifice and 20 g of the mixture weighed into each of two lusteroid centrifuge tubes, 10 cm long and 2.5 cm in diameter. 20 ml of the starting microsomal preparation, containing 0.25 M sucrose, 0.001 M MgCl$_2$, and K$_2$HPO$_4$ were then added to each tube. The tubes were inverted several times and run in a Wifug R centrifuge at 10.000 r.p.m. (8000 g at av. radius) for 45 minutes in order to obtain phase separation. The volumes of the bottom and top phases were about 11 and 29 ml respectively. The bottom phase was turbid and pink in colour and contained a thin pellet consisting of larger particles and aggregated material which had sedimented, The top phase was colourless and slightly turbid. 22 g of the top phase were removed from each tube, employing a pipette with a bent tip, and replaced by 27 g of fresh top phase obtained from two blanks run in parallel. The distribution was then repeated and 27 g of top phase from each tube were taken out. The top phases from the two distributions were combined (93 g, the rest being left on the pipette walls) and mixed with, first 2 g of 10 per cent (w/w) D68 and then 41.2 g of 3 per cent (w/w) MC4000 in 0.001 M MgCl$_2$ and K$_2$HPO$_4$, to obtain a system of 0.50 per cent dextran and 1.2 per cent methylcellulose (system D of Fig. 6.2). This mixture was centrifuged at 10,000 r.p.m. for 30 minutes. The bottom phase, which

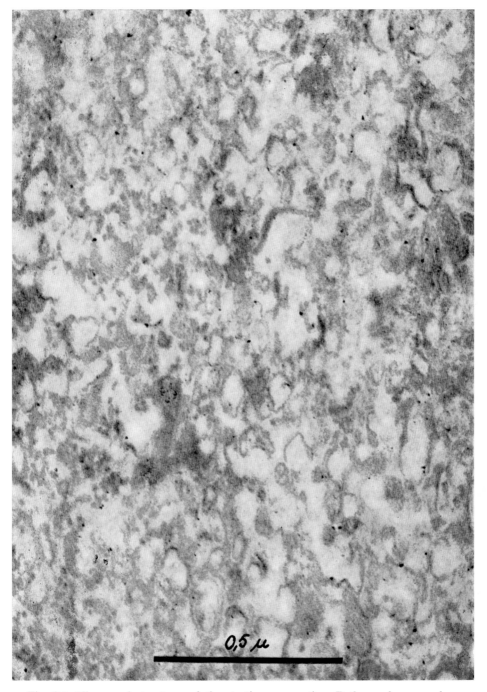

Fig. 6.4. Microsomal structures of the starting preparation. Both membranes and particles are visible. ×100,000. From ref. (1).

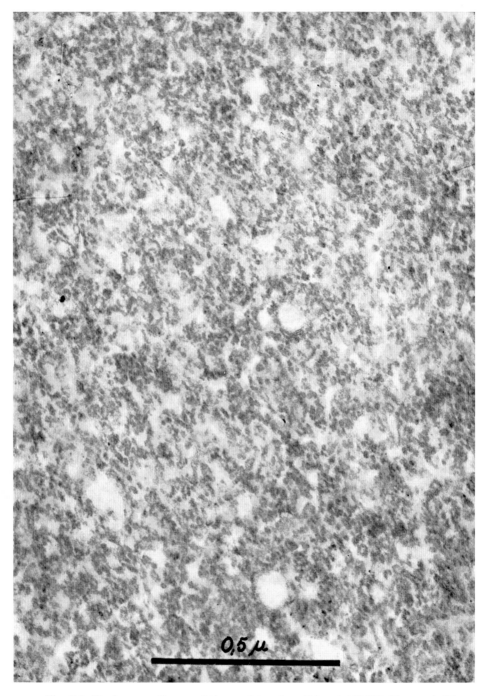

Fig. 6.5. Final preparation consisting mainly of particles. ×100,000. From ref. (1).

TABLE 6.1. *Protein and ribonucleic acid content of the two preparations indicated in Fig. 6.3. Compare with morphological aspects in Figs. 6.4 and 6.5. Protein was determined by the method of Lowry et al. (5) and ribonucleic acid by the method of Littlefield et al. (3, 10). From ref. (1).*

| | | Protein | | RNA | | |
	Experiment no.	Total mg	(Yield %)	Total mg	(Yield %)	Concentration (μg/mg of protein)
Starting Preparation (Supernate of brain homogenate, centrifuged	1	344		9.8		28.5
15 min at 18 000 g)	2	368		10.8		29.4
Final Preparation	1	4.8	(1.4)	0.68	(6.9)	142
	2	4.6	(1.3)	0.77	(7.2)	168

was slightly turbid, was collected through a small hole bored in the bottom of the centrifuge tubes. The total volume of the bottom phase was 14 ml and was diluted to 24 ml with 0.001 M $MgCl_2$ and K_2HPO_4 and centrifuged in a Spinco model L centrifuge, rotor No. 40 at 40,000 r.p.m. for 2 hours. The pellet was resuspended in a small volume.

Electron micrographs of sectioned pellets of the starting and final preparations treated with osmium tetroxide (1) are shown in Figs. 6.4 and 6.5. As may be seen, the final preparation consists mainly of particles almost free of vesicles.

Table 6.1 shows the protein and ribonucleic acid content of the two fractions. The yield of ribonucleic acid was 6–8 per cent of the total ribonucleic acid of the starting preparation. As this includes 15–20 per cent of "soluble", unsedimentable ribonucleic acid, the yield was 8–10 per cent of the particulate ribonucleic acid. This low yield suggests that the greater part of the ribonucleoprotein particles are attached to the membranes and/or aggregated in clusters, since they would then remain in the bottom phase of system A1. Some aggregation of the particles was actually observed in samples from this phase.

The starting preparation consisted of the whole supernate from rat brain tissue homogenized with 4 volumes of buffered sucrose and centrifuged at 18 000 g for 15 minutes. Thus it contained both the microsomal structures and the soluble cytoplasmic fraction, the isolation scheme providing the separation of the latter in the final step. The microsomal structures had therefore not been packed into a pellet by high speed centrifugation before the fractionation procedure. This is a particular advantage since packing by centrifugation in many cases causes irreversible aggregation. This seems to be a general experience.

The fact that the experimental results are in agreement with the hypothetical separation, as described by Fig. 6.1, does not necessarily mean that this mechanism of separation is correct. Not only the surface areas of the particles, but also specific properties of the particle surfaces, may have determined the distribution.

REFERENCES

1. ALBERTSSON, P. Å., HANZON, V., and TOSCHI, G., *J. Ultrastructure Res.*, *2*, 366 (1959).
2. HANZON, V., and TOSCHI, G., *Exptl. Cell Res.*, *16*, 256 (1959).
3. LITTLEFIELD, J. W., KELLER, E. B., GROSS, J., and Zamecnik, P. C., *J. Biol. Chem.*, *217*, 111 (1955).
4. LOFTFIELD, R. B., *Progr. in Biophys.*, *8*, 348 (1957).
5. LOWRY, O. H., ROSEBROUGH, N. J., FARR, A. L., and RANDALL, R. J., *J. Biol. Chem.*, *193*, 265 (1951).
6. PALADE, G. E., and SIEKEVITZ, P., *J. Biophys. Biochem. Cytol.*, *2*, 171 (1956).
7. PORTER, K. R., and KALLMANN, F. L., *Ann. N.Y. Acad. Sci.*, *54*, 882 (1952).
8. SJÖSTRAND, F. S., and HANZON, V., *Exptl. Cell Res.*, *7*, 393 (1954).
9. SJÖSTRAND, F. S., *in* Physical Techniques in Biological Research, edited by Oster, G. and Pollister A. W., Vol. 3, p. 241, Academic Press, New York, 1956.
10. TOSCHI, G., *Exptl. Cell Res.*, *16*, 232 (1959).

7. Concentration and Purification of Viruses

INTRODUCTION

Many interesting biochemical substances are present in nature at very low concentrations and to obtain weighable amounts one has to isolate them from large quantities of material. Viruses, and particularly the animal viruses, are examples of such substances which occur naturally in extremely low concentrations. Even if a virus culture is biologically highly active, it contains a very small amount of virus as mg virus/ml; thus in a tissue culture, the number of virus particles may be of the order of 10^7 per ml. If one assumes the virus particles to be 100 mμ in diameter and their density to be 1.3, a calculation will show that 1 ml of a suspension with 10^7 virus particles contains only about 7×10^{-9} g virus. The concentration of the virus from large volumes of such a dilute suspension into a small volume is therefore an important step in the purification procedure. A two-phase system is apparently able to carry out such a concentration, provided it can be constructed in such a way that most of the virus particles are transferred to a phase with a small volume compared to that of the original virus culture and that the viruses are not inactivated by the phase system. In this chapter, it will be shown how it is possible to construct such a phase system by using water-soluble polymers. Moreover, it has been found that other substances than viruses, such as proteins and cell fragments, usually distribute in a different manner in the phase systems and are therefore more or less eliminated during the concentration process (6, 7, 12, 14); a concentration and a purification of the virus is thus obtained at the same time.

Concentration may be effected by one-step procedures or by multistep procedures.

THE ONE-STEP PROCEDURE

The principle for the concentration in one step is that solutions of two polymers are added to the particle suspension so that a small

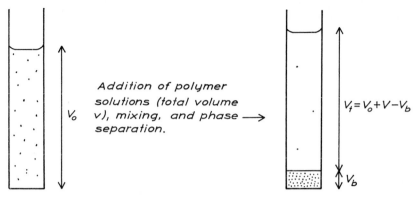

Fig. 7.1. The principle for the concentration of virus particles in a two-phase system. Solutions of polymers are added to the virus suspension having a volume of V_0, in such proportions that a small phase is formed in which the particles are concentrated. The points represent virus particles.

volume phase is obtained containing most of the particles; see Fig. 7.1. Suppose that the volume of the original particle suspension is V_0 ml and that the concentration of its particles is C_0 particles per ml. The two polymer solutions with a total volume of v are then added to the particle suspension to get the desired phase system. After mixing and phase separation, a bottom phase with a volume of V_b is formed; the volume of the top phase is then

$$V_t = V_0 + v - V_b. \tag{1}$$

If the particles distribute with a partition coefficient K, and no adsorption occurs at the interface, i.e.

$$K = \frac{C_t}{C_b}, \tag{2}$$

where C_t and C_b are the concentrations of the particles in the top and bottom phases respectively, the number of particles present in the top phase, together with the number present in the bottom phase, should equal the number of particles in the original solution, i.e.

$$V_t \cdot C_t + V_b \cdot C_b = V_0 \cdot C_0. \tag{3}$$

We are mainly interested in knowing two things. The first is the concentration effect of the system; this is the concentration of virus particles in the virus-rich phase, in this case the bottom phase, compared with the concentration of virus particles in the original suspension. The second is the yield of virus particles in the virus-rich phase.

The Concentrating Effect

As a measure of the concentration effect of a system, we use the concentrating factor α which is defined as

$$\alpha = \frac{C_b}{C_0}. \tag{4}$$

This may be calculated from eqns. (2) and (3) and becomes

$$\alpha = \frac{V_0}{V_b\left(1 + \frac{V_t}{V_b} \cdot K\right)}. \tag{5}$$

To obtain large α values, i.e. a good concentrating effect of the system, V_b should be small compared to V_0, K should be small, and V_t should not be too large compared with V_0, i.e. v should be as small as possible.

From eqn. (5) we also learn that if the ratio of the volumes of the two phases in a given system is kept constant, the concentrating factor will be larger the smaller the partition coefficient K of the particles, until a value of $\alpha = V_0/V_b$ is approached when $K \to 0$.

If for a system, V_0, v, and K are kept constant, but V_b is decreased, then α will increase and approach a value of $1/K \cdot (V_0/V_t)$ as $V_b \to 0$.

The Yield of Concentrated Particles

The yield, y, of the concentrated particles is expressed as per cent of the total amount of particles, i.e.

$$y = 100 \cdot \frac{C_b \cdot V_b}{C_0 \cdot V_0}, \tag{6a}$$

or

$$y = 100 \cdot \alpha \cdot \frac{V_b}{V_0}, \tag{6b}$$

or

$$y = \frac{100}{1 + \frac{V_t}{V_b} \cdot K}. \tag{6c}$$

TABLE 7.1. *The yield (y) and concentration factor (α) of a system, calculated from eqns. 5 and 6 c with $V_0 = 1000$ ml, $v = 100$ ml, $K = 0.001$, for different V_b values.*

V_b, ml	y, %	α
100	99	9.9
10	90	90
1	48	480

TABLE 7.2. *The minimum volume of the bottom phase (V_b), and the corresponding concentration factor (α), which allow a concentration of 90 per cent of the virus particles in the bottom phase. Calculated from eqns. 5 and 6 c for different K values; $V_0 = 1000$ ml; $v = 100$ ml; $y = 90$ per cent.*

K	V_b, ml	α
0.1	521	1.7
0.01	91	10
0.005	47.4	19
0.001	9.8	92
0.0005	4.9	183
0.0001	0.99	910

From these equations we learn that, when the volume ratio is constant, the yield becomes greater the smaller K.

However, for constant K, V_0 and v, the yield becomes less the smaller V_b (eqn. 6 c). Therefore for a system where K is given, one has to compromise between the increasing concentrating effect (eqn. 5) and a decreasing yield (eqn. 6 c) when V_b is made smaller; see also Table 7.1, where the yield and the concentration factor have been calculated for systems with different bottom phase volumes.

If one requires a yield above a certain value, for example 90 per cent, there will then be for each K value a lower limit to the volume of the bottom phase which has the maximum concentrating effect. These values have been calculated for a system with $V_0 = 1000$ ml and $v = 100$ ml, and are given in Table 7.2.

The above calculations apply to systems in which the virus particles are concentrated into the bottom phase. Relations which apply to systems in which the virus particles are concentrated into the top phase may be obtained by exchanging V_b and V_t and by replacing K with $1/K$ in the above equations.

The Selection of a Phase System

The composition of a phase system suitable for concentration should be represented by a point on the phase diagram which is far enough from the critical point to represent a stable system and to allow a one-sided distribution without adsorption at the interface. To get a small phase, the point representing the mixture should be near the binodial, for example, point A of Fig. 7.2. In addition, the time of phase separation should be short and it should be possible to add the polymers as concentrated solutions so that v (see eqns. above) can be made small.

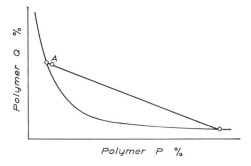

Fig. 7.2. To obtain a phase system with one phase small compared to the other, the total composition of the system should be represented by a point lying close to the binodial, such as point A of this figure. In this case, the polymer P-rich phase will be the smaller.

To find a system which fulfills these requirements, one may proceed as follows. If the phase diagram of a system is known, one first determines the K value for the particles in a series of mixtures represented by points increasingly removed from the critical point, for example, points 1, 2, 3, 4, and 5 in Fig. 7.3. A system which gives a one-sided distribution and which is not too far away from the critical point is then selected. Suppose, for example, that points 3, 4, and 5 give a fully one-sided distribution of the particles; of these systems the one represented by point 3 is far enough from the critical point to be a stable system but not too far from it to have phases which are too viscous. A system with a small phase is therefore selected from a point lying on the tie line going through point 3. For example, a number of systems represented by points a, b, c, and d (Fig. 7.3) are set up and the one with a suitably small phase is selected. Some of these points may lie outside the binodial because, for systems with polydisperse polymers, there is not a sharp change from a one-phase system to a two-phase system such as indicated by the binodial; see Chapter 2, "Influence of Polydispersity of the Polymers". Experiments which illustrate how a suitable system may be selected in the way described above are given in Tables 7.4 and 7.5. Each series of systems listed in these tables is represented by points lying approximately on the same tie line, that is they correspond to points a, b, c, and d in Fig. 7.3.

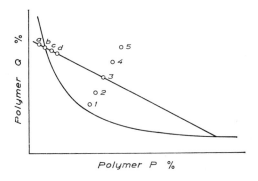

Fig. 7.3. To obtain a system like point P of Fig. 7.2, which also allows a concentration of virus particles, one may proceed as follows: the partition of the virus is first determined in systems represented by the points 1, 2, 3, 4, and 5. If, for example, system 3 gives a fully one-sided distribution, a number of systems a, b, c, d, on the tie line going through point 3 are tested to find which gives a suitably small phase in which the particles are concentrated.

If a phase diagram is not available, a suitable system may be obtained in the following way. First, an attempt is made to discover for which phase the particles have the greatest affinity. Suppose in a system of the two polymers P and Q the particles go to the P-rich phase. A series of mixtures of different concentrations, for example, 0.1, 0.5, 1.0, 1.5 ... per cent of polymer P and each with increasing amounts of polymer Q is then set up. Those systems which have a small P polymer phase are then tested to see if they give K values which allow an efficient concentration.

Recent studies (3, 6, 14) have demonstrated that larger virus particles, such as the T-even phages, vaccinia virus, myxo viruses, and adeno virus are well concentrated in the dextran–methylcellulose

TABLE 7.3. *Phase systems which allow an efficient concentration of viruses.*

Phase system	Virus tested	Virus-rich phase	Reference
Dextran–methylcellulose	Phage T2 and T4	Bottom	3, 6
	Adeno	Bottom	14
	Influenza	Bottom	14
	Parotitis	Bottom	14
	Newcastle disease	Bottom	14
	Vaccinia	Bottom	14
Na dextran sulfate– methylcellulose	Phage T2	Bottom	7, 12
	Adeno	Bottom	12
	Influenza	Bottom	12
Dextran–polyethylene glycol	ECHO	Bottom and interface	14
	Phage T2	Interface	
	Adeno	Interface	14
	Influenza	Interface	14
	Parotitis	Interface	14
	Newcastle Disease	Interface	14
	Vaccinia	Interface	14
	Tobacco mosaic	Top or interface	
Na dextran sulfate–poly- ethylene glycol	Phage T2	Top or	12
	ECHO	bottom	12
	Polio	depending	11
	Adeno	on the salt concentration	12
Na dextran sulfate–poly- vinyl alcohol	ECHO	Bottom	12

system. The same holds for the Na dextran sulfate–methylcellulose system (12). Smaller virus particles as phage T3, tobacco mosaic virus, and in particular ECHO (enteric cytopathogenic human orphan) virus and polio virus are not concentrated to the same extent in these systems (12, 14). (Compositions of these systems very far removed from the critical point cannot be used because the phases would be too viscous.)

In the dextran–polyethylene glycol system, the larger virus particles are mainly adsorbed at the interface (14), (a phenomenon which may also be used for concentration purposes) while ECHO virus goes to the bottom phase or the interface, depending on the salt content.

In the Na dextran sulfate–polyethylene glycol system, all viruses so far tested can be concentrated in one of the phases; the bottom phase at lower salt concentrations (0.15–0.3 M NaCl) and the top phase at higher salt concentrations (1 M NaCl) (11, 12).

Finally, in the Na dextran sulfate–polyvinylalcohol system, all viruses presently tested are concentrated into the bottom phase (12).

In Table 7.3 all phase systems which have been tested and proved to give an efficient concentration of the viruses are recorded.

The Time of Phase Separation

The time taken for the small bottom phase to form and settle in a number of phase systems is given in Figs. 7.4–7.7. The settling time is shorter for the systems containing polyethylene glycol (Figs. 7.4 and 7.5) than for those containing methylcellulose (Figs. 7.6 and 7.7); it also becomes longer the smaller the bottom phase. Compare, for example, the two curves of Figs. 7.4 and 7.5. These two systems had about the same compositions of the phases and about the same height but differed in the volume ratio; the former system had a bottom phase volume of about 1/22 the latter about 1/110 of the total phase system. The time necessary for the settling of 90 per cent of the bottom phase was about 2.5 hours for the system of Fig. 7.4 and about 20 hours for the system of Fig. 7.5.

The settling time decreases with increasing temperature, mainly

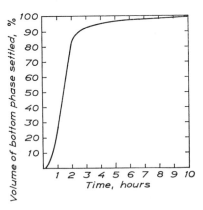

Fig. 7.4. The volume of the bottom phase settled, in per cent of total bottom phase, as a function of time for 100 g of a system of 1 % (w/w) NaDS 70 and 6.45 % (w/w) PEG 6000 in 0.3 M NaCl at 4°C. The total volume of the bottom phase is 4.5 ml.

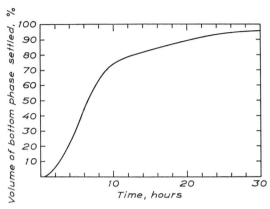

Fig. 7.5. The volume of the bottom phase settled, in per cent of total bottom phase, as a function of time for 1000 g of a system of 0.2 % (w/w) NaDS 70 and 6.45 % (w/w) PEG 6000 in 0.3 M NaCl at 4°C. The total volume of the bottom phase is 9.0 ml.

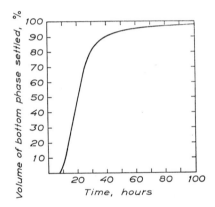

Fig. 7.6. Volume of the bottom phase settled, in per cent of total bottom phase, as a function of time for 100 g of a system of 0.22 % (w/w) NaDS 70 and 0.51 % (w/w) MC 4000 in 0.15 M NaCl at 4°C. The total volume of the bottom phase is 7.2 ml.

because the viscosity of the top phases decreases; this decrease in settling time at higher temperatures is very pronounced for the methylcellulose-containing systems.

Concentration Effect and Volume Ratio

To investigate experimentally how much a virus suspension may be concentrated by one step, phage T2 and ECHO virus were concentrated in a number of systems with varying volume ratios.[1] The results

---

[1] The titre determinations of phage T2 and ECHO virus were kindly carried out by Drs. G. Frick and L. Philipson.

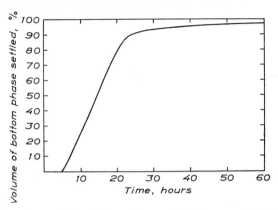

Fig. 7.7. The volume of the bottom phase settled, in per cent of total bottom phase, as a function of time for 100 g of a system of 0.48 % (w/w) D 68 and 0.44 % (w/w) MC 4000 in 0.15 M NaCl at 4°C. The total volume of the bottom phase is 11.5 ml.

TABLE 7.4. *Experimental and theoretical values of the concentration factor (α) and the yield (y) for phage T2 in Na dextran sulfate–methylcellulose systems with decreasing volumes of the bottom phase. The theoretical values are calculated from eqns. 5 and 6 c for $V_0 = 99$ ml; $v = 0$ ml; $K = 0.5 \times 10^{-2}$. Temperature: $4°C$.*

Polymer composition[1] (in 0.15 M NaCl)				α		$y, \%$	
NaDS 68 % w/w	MC 4000 % w/w	$K \times 10^{+2}$	V_b ml	experi- mental	theore- tical	experi- mental	theore- tical
0.19	0.52	0.50	9.8	9.8	9.64	95	96
0.16	0.53	0.59	7.9	13	11.9	98	94
0.13	0.54	0.64	5.2	18	17.5	102	92
0.10	0.55	0.5	2.8	27	30.2	75	86
0.08	0.56	1.1	0.5	37	100	18.4	50

[1] See Fig. 2.35.

are presented in Tables 7.4 and 7.5. Thus phage T2 was distributed in a number of Na dextran sulfate–methylcellulose systems with compositions on approximately the same tie line but with decreasing bottom phase volumes. In Table 7.4, the experimental K values, concentration factors, and yields are recorded, together with the theoretical concentration factors and yields calculated for a K value of 0.5×10^{-2}. It can be seen that all systems, except the last, give a concentration factor and a yield in fairly good agreement with the theoretical values. It is thus possible to concentrate up to about 30 times with a high

TABLE 7.5. *Partition coefficient, K, of ECHO virus in Na dextran sulfate–polyethylene glycol systems with decreasing volumes of the bottom phase; in 0.3 M NaCl at 4°C. Compare with Fig. 7.3. PFU = plaque forming units. Total volume = 200 ml.*

No.	Phase system[1] NaDS 68 % w/w	PEG 6000 % w/w	Bottom phase volume ml	Titre of top phase PFU/ml	Titre of bottom phase PFU/ml	K
1	1	6.0	10.0	5.3×10^3	8.5×10^6	6.2×10^{-4}
2	0.8	6.1	8.8	2.8×10^3	8.8×10^6	3.2×10^{-4}
3	0.6	6.2	7.0	5.8×10^3	1.1×10^7	5.3×10^{-4}
4	0.4	6.3	3.5	6.3×10^3	1.8×10^7	8.5×10^{-4}
5	0.2	6.4	1.9	1.1×10^4	2.3×10^7	4.8×10^{-4}
6	0.1	6.45	0.8	1.0×10^5	7×10^7	1.4×10^{-3}

[1] See Fig. 2.34.

yield in a Na dextran sulfate–methylcellulose system. The same holds for the dextran–methylcellulose system.

An analogous experiment with ECHO virus in an Na dextran sulfate–polyethylene glycol system is recorded in Table 7.5. In this case, the concentration factor is of the same order for all systems except the last (no. 6). The determination of the activity of this virus is not sufficiently accurate, (each titre determination may have an error of about ± 50 per cent) to allow any conclusion about the yield. System no. 5 has been used for the concentration of a large volume of ECHO virus culture and of polio virus (see section 3 below).

In the calculation of the theoretical concentration factors and yields it has been assumed that the two phases have been completely separated. In practice, however, this is not the case since droplets of the bottom phase may remain in the top phase for a long time. This occurs more in the systems containing methylcellulose than in the others (see also Figs. 7.4–7.7).

Thus, in conclusion, there are both theoretical and practical limitations to the concentration effect and to the yield of concentrated particles which can be obtained from a system in one operation. To obtain a yield of 80–100 per cent, the bottom phase should have a volume not less than 1/30 of the total for the dextran–methylcellulose or the dextran sulfate–methylcellulose systems, and a volume not less than 1/100 of the total for the dextran sulfate–polyethylene glycol system.

Technique

Phase separation is usually allowed to take place in a conventional separating funnel. A convenient model, which may be used when the bottom phase volume is very small, is shown in Fig. 7.8. The bottom phase settles in the narrow, graduated tube and its formation may be easily followed visually. The bottom phase is collected by allowing

Fig. 7.8. Separating funnel for concentration of virus into a small volume of bottom phase.

it to pass slowly through the outlet. An advantage of this model is that during this procedure the surface of the phase boundary does not decrease, which would otherwise cause material attached to the phase boundary to drag down into the bottom phase.

The polymers are added in the form of solutions; these are made as concentrated as possible to reduce the dilution of the virus culture. Methylcellulose may conveniently be added as a slurry in a concentrated salt solution; see section 6 below. Dextran sulfate may be precipitated by adding barium or potassium ions. The efficiency of the precipitation with $BaCl_2$ and KCl is shown by Figs. 7.14–7.16. Further experimental details are given below for each experiment.

Application

Polymer phase systems have already been used for the concentration and purification of a number of viruses. A few typical one-step procedures which have been previously published (6, 7, 11, 12, 14), will now be described in detail.

1. Isolation of Phage T2 by a Na Dextran sulfate–Methylcellulose System and Subsequent Treatment with "Freon 113" and Precipitation of Dextran Sulfate with BaCl₂ or KCl (7, 12)

Concentration. Echerichia coli, strain 13, is grown in 2000 ml of a Friedlein buffer in a container of stainless steel with a device for good aeration, thermostated at 37°C. When the titre of $E.$ $coli$ is about 10^8, judged from the absorption at 600 mμ in the Beckman B spectrophotometer, enough phages are added to bring the phage titre up to about 10^7. 6–9 hours later the medium becomes fairly clear and the phage titre $3\text{–}6 \times 10^{10}$. Due to evaporation losses during the cultivation, the weight of the culture medium has reduced about 10 per cent. The culture medium is transferred to a separating funnel, put in the cold room (8°C) and solutions of Na dextran sulfate and methylcellulose added to a final concentration of 0.22 per cent (w/w) of NaDS 68 and 0.51 per cent (w/w) of MC 4000. (15 g of a 20 per cent (w/w) solution of NaDS 68 and 347 g of a 2 per cent (w/w) solution of MC 4000 are therefore added to each 1000 g of culture medium.) The contents are thoroughly mixed by inverting the funnel several times and the system then allowed to stand for 36–48 hours for phase separation. The settling time of this system is recorded in Fig. 7.6. The bottom phase formed has a volume of 1/15 to 1/13 of the original phage culture and contains most of the phages.

Thus an experiment (7), in which the original phage culture had a volume of 1530 ml with a titre of 4.5×10^{10}, gave a bottom phase with a volume of 120 ml and a titre of 4.4×10^{11}, i.e. a concentration factor of 9.8 and a yield of 77 per cent. The upper part of the top phase had a titre of 1.8×10^9.

Assuming a K value of 0.005 for the phages in this phase system, we may calculate the theoretical concentration factor and yield. Thus

$$K = 0.005$$
$$V_0 = 1530 \text{ ml}$$
$$v = 23 + 535 \text{ ml}$$
$$V_B = 120 \text{ ml}$$

Putting these values in eqn. (5) we should expect a concentration factor of 11.8 (experimentally found 9.8) and a yield of 92 per cent (experimentally found 77 per cent). The difference between the experimental and theoretical concentration factors is within the error of the phage titre determination since this is not very accurate for the crude lysates used here. The lower experimental yield, however, is partly due to incomplete separation of the phases. As may be seen in Fig. 7.6, part of the bottom phase of the Na dextran sulfate–methylcellulose system still remains in the form of droplets in the top phase after 36 hours phase separation. This has been confirmed by taking samples from the lower part of the top phase, just above the phase boundary, after 36 hours phase separation. These samples have given titres 5–10 times higher than samples from the upper part of the top phase (7). The yield may be increased by allowing a longer time of phase separation.

"*Freon*" *treatment.* Particulate fragments of the lysed bacteria together with unlysed bacteria also concentrate in the bottom phase, while soluble constituents like proteins distribute more evenly and are therefore partly eliminated by the concentration step. In order to remove the major part of the impurities in the bottom phase it is treated with a fluorocarbon "Freon 113" according to methods described earlier (6, 8). To reduce losses the following procedure according to Frick (7), is recommended.

The bottom phase is transferred to a beaker and NaCl added to a concentration of 0.5 *M*. (This probably dissociates some phages attached to bacterial fragments which are otherwise removed by the Freon treatment (7).) The suspension is then vigorously agitated by a blender operated at high speed for 4×15 seconds. One-third of the volume of "Freon 113" is then added. The blender is next operated at high speed for 4×15 seconds with intervening pauses of 30 seconds. After this treatment, the suspension is centrifuged at 1000 g for 10 minutes. The layer of denatured protein and "Freon" will form a semi-solid pellet and the supernate can easily be decanted. The procedure is then repeated 3 times. By this procedure the phages withstand the "Freon" treatment fairly well. The losses are in the range of 10–20 per cent including those due to manipulation of the liquids. If, however, the salt concentration is not raised, losses of as much as 50 per cent may occur.

The bottom phase, before the "Freon" treatment, contains 1.15 per cent (w/w) Na dextran sulfate and 0.2 per cent (w/w) methylcellulose (see Fig. 2.35). The major part of the methylcellulose, but not the Na dextran sulfate, is removed from the aqueous phase by the "Freon" treatment (12).

An interesting finding is that Na dextran sulfate, like dextran (6), has a protective effect, since "Freon" treatment of phages suspended in an inorganic medium only (Friedlein buffer) results in a drop in titre of about 10^3 for each treatment (6).

Precipitation with BaCl$_2$ or KCl. To remove the 1.15 per cent Na dextran sulfate present in the "Freon" treated phage suspension, 0.038 ml 1 M BaCl$_2$ (plus the volume of 1 M BaCl$_2$ which is necessary for precipitation of the phosphate in the buffer) or 0.12 ml 4 M KCl is added to each ml phage suspension. A heavy precipitate is formed, centrifuged off and the clear supernatant liquid dialyzed against 0.15 M NaCl and 0.0008 M MgCl$_2$ for 12 hours to remove excess salt and low molecular constituents. No significant loss in titre occurs with these procedures.

The yield of phages obtained by this method is about 60–70 per cent.

The phages may now be recovered by centrifugation (7) or they may be further concentrated and purified by a second distribution in the same phase system. This second step will be described below (section 4).

Either NaDS 68 or NaDS 70 may be used for the experiments described above, the phase systems with the two NaDS fractions being rather similar.

2. *Concentration of Phage T2 by a Dextran–Methylcellulose System (6)*

The phage cultivation is carried out in the same way as described in the previous experiment. For concentration, solutions of dextran and methylcellulose are added to give a final concentration of 0.48 per cent (w/w) D 68 and 0.44 per cent (w/w) MC 4000. (For compositions of the two phases see (Fig. 2.27.) Thus in one experiment the following mixture was prepared:

phage culture with a titre of 5×10^{10}	2000 g
10 per cent (w/w) D 68	131 g
2 per cent (w/w) MC 4000	601 g

After mixing and 36–48 hours phase separation in the cold room (4°C), a bottom phase with a volume of about 200 ml had formed. (The settling time for this system is given in Fig. 7.7.) It had a titre of 5×10^{11}, i.e. a concentration factor of about 10 and a yield of 96–97 per cent. These experimental values are in good agreement with what one expects from theory. Thus, in this experiment

$$K = 0.0025 \text{ (see Table 4.7)}$$
$$V_0 = 2000$$
$$v = 601 + 131$$
$$V_B = 200$$

Putting these values in eqn. (5) we should expect a concentration factor of 9.7; experimentally a value of about 10 was found. In the same way the yield should be, by putting the values above in eqn. (6c), 97 per cent in agreement with the 96–97 per cent found experimentally.

3. *ECHO Virus and Polio Virus in a Na Dextran Sulfate–Polyethylene Glycol System*

ECHO virus (12)

ECHO virus, prototype 7, grown in monkey kidney cultures with Parker 199 as maintainance medium, is concentrated in the following way. Solutions of Na dextran sulfate, polyethylene glycol, and sodium chloride are added to the virus culture to give a final composition of 0.2 per cent (w/w) NaDS 68 and 6.45 per cent (w/w) PEG 6000 in 0.3 M NaCl. This mixture is represented by system C in Fig. 2.34.

Thus in one experiment the following mixture was prepared:

virus culture	5000 ml
20 per cent (w/w) NaDS 68	64 g
30 per cent (w/w) PEG 6000 containing 69.5 g NaCl	1390 g

Since the culture medium originally contains about 0.15 M NaCl, the final NaCl concentration will be 0.3 M. The mixture is put into a

TABLE 7.6. *Concentration and purification (Step 1) of ECHO virus type 7 from
5 litres of virus culture by distribution in a phase system composed of 0.2 % (w/w)
Na dextran sulfate (NaDS 68) and 6.45 % (w/w) polyethylene glycol (PEG 6000)
in 0.3 M NaCl. Data from ref. (12).*

Preparation	Volume ml	Infectivity TCD 50/ml log units	Con-centration factor	Mg N/ml by Kjeldahl	TCD 50/g protein log units
Original virus culture	5000	7.3	1	0.218	10.2
Bottom phase (Step 1)	50	9.3	100	0.790	11.6
Top phase (Step 1)	6400	5.9		0.155	

separating funnel, mixed, and allowed to stand for 24 hours in the cold
room (4°C) for phase separation. The settling time for this system is
given in Fig. 7.5. The results of the above experiment are recorded in
Table 7.6. Practically all of the virus activity has been concentrated
into the small bottom phase which has a volume of one-hundredth
of the original virus culture. Thus a concentration factor of about 100
and a yield of about 100 per cent were obtained. These figures are,
however, very approximate since the determination of virus activity
is not very accurate. In this experiment

$$K = 10^{-3.4}$$
$$V_0 = 5000 \text{ ml}$$
$$v = 1430 \text{ ml}$$
$$V_B = 50 \text{ ml}$$

By putting these values in eqns. (5) and (6c) we should expect a concentration factor of 99 and a yield of 99 per cent.

The bottom phase was clear, while large amounts of particulate
material collected at the interface.

The concentration of Na dextran sulfate in the bottom phase of this
system is 17 per cent (w/w) as seen in the phase diagram (Fig. 2.34);
to remove this, 0.67 ml 3 M KCl are added to each g of the bottom
phase; a heavy precipitate of dextran sulfate forms and the viruses
remain in the supernate.

By centrifugation at high speed in the Spinco ultracentrifuge, a
translucent pellet has been obtained which was examined with the

TABLE 7.7. *Concentration of polio virus (Step 1) in a two-phase system of Na dextran sulfate and polyethylene glycol (the same composition as in Table 7.6). Data from ref. (11).*

Preparation	Volume ml	Infectivity TCD 50/ml log units	Con-centration factor	Total amount of virus, TCD 50
Original virus culture	100	7.5	1	3.2×10^9
Bottom phase (Step 1)	1.2	9.4	80	3.0×10^9
Top phase (Step 1)	134	5.6		5.2×10^7

electron microscope (9, 12). It consisted mainly of particles 17–22 mμ in diameter, of which parts were arranged in crystalline structure. Particles of similar size have been observed with the electron microscope when the virus preparation was sprayed and shadowed (4).

It is apparent that a very efficient concentration of ECHO virus may be obtained by the dextran sulfate–polyethylene glycol system in one simple operation. A considerable purification is also obtained at the same time since the specific infectivity in terms of titre per g protein has increased about 25 times; see Table 7.6. Electron microscopy (4) has also indicated a high degree of purification.

The virus may be further concentrated and purified by a second step; see below, section 5.

Polio virus

The same polymer composition as described above for ECHO virus has been used for concentration of polio virus (11). The following mixture was prepared:

virus culture	100 g
20 per cent (w/w) NaDS 70	1.34 g
30 per cent (w/w) PEG 6000	29.0 g
5 M NaCl	5.0 g

Since the virus culture contains 0.15 M NaCl the final NaCl concentration will be 0.3 M. A typical experiment is recorded in Table 7.7. As can be seen, almost all the virus activity is found in the bottom phase and is thus concentrated about 80 times. The dextran sulfate of the bottom phase may be precipitated with KCl, as described above for ECHO virus, without loss in virus activity.

Either NaDS 68 or NaDS 70 may be used for the experiments described above, the phase systems with the two NaDS fractions being rather similar.

MULTISTEP PROCEDURES

As was shown above, it is not suitable to concentrate more than 30–100 times in one step if a high yield is desired. By using a multistep method, however, a higher concentration effect may be achieved. There are many different ways in which such a multistep concentration may be carried out. Some which have been applied practically will be described below.

I. Repeated Concentration after Removal of the Polymer in the Virus-Rich Phase

The principle of this method is as follows. The virus particles are first concentrated into a small phase of a given phase system. The polymer which is present in this phase is then removed in some way from the virus suspension. A new phase system, similar to the first, is then set up and the virus particles are concentrated into a still smaller volume. Theoretically, this procedure may then be repeated an infinite number of times.

Systems which allow a concentration according to this principle are, for example, those containing dextran sulfate, which can easily be removed by precipitation with $BaCl_2$ or KCl. An example of such a concentration of phage T2 in Na dextran sulfate–methylcellulose is described below. (Another phase system which could be used is the potassium phosphate–polyethylene glycol system in which the salt may be removed by dialysis. This system has not yet been tested.)

Application

4. Bacteriophage T2 in the Na Dextran Sulfate–Methylcellulose System (7, 12)

Step 1 is identical with Exp. 1, described under "One-Step Procedures". Its final product in one experiment was 50 g of a phage sus-

TABLE 7.8. *Properties of phage T2 preparations obtained using a Na dextran sulfate–methylcellulose system. Data according to ref. (7).*
corr. = corrected for light scattering.

E_{260}/E_{280}	1.38 ± 0.02
E_{260} corr./E_{280} corr.	1.40 ± 0.02
E_{260} corr./10^{12} plaques	6.0 ± 0.2
$\mu g\ N/10^{12}$ plaques	$94 \quad \pm 2$
$\mu g\ P/10^{12}$ plaques	$28 \quad \pm 1$
$\mu g\ N/\mu g\ P$	3.3 ± 0.1

pension dialyzed against 0.15 M NaCl, 0.001 M MgCl$_2$, and having a titre of 1.9×10^{11}.

Step 2. The phage suspension is transferred to a smaller separating funnel and Na dextran sulfate and methylcellulose are added to give the same phase system as in Step 1, i.e. 0.22 per cent (w/w) NaDS 68 and 0.51 per cent (w/w) MC 4000. Thus the 50 g of the phage suspension are mixed with 0.75 g 20 per cent (w/w) NaDS 68 and 17.3 g 2 per cent (w/w) MC 4000. After mixing, the system is allowed to stand for 36–48 hours in the cold for phase separation. A bottom phase with a volume of 3–5 ml has then formed and contains most of the phages. A majority of the latter precipitates and is found in the lower part of the bottom phase. This fraction, which will be called fraction P, accounts for more than 90 per cent of all phages and is collected by slow speed centrifugation; a loose pellet is obtained which can easily be resuspended in 0.15 M NaCl and 0.001 M MgCl$_2$.

Analysis of fraction P has revealed that this consists of almost pure phages (7). Thus, in the ultracentrifuge, 97–100 per cent of the UV absorbing material sediments together with the phage boundary. The sedimentation constant S_{20w}, is 1000–1150 S or 730 S depending on the ionic composition and pH (7). The optical density per 10^{12} plaques and the chemical analysis are recorded in Table 7.8. These values agree well with earlier data obtained with phages prepared by other methods (7). It should be pointed out that these properties of the preparation are highly reproducible.

The rest of the phages of the bottom phase remain in suspension above the precipitated fraction P. The reason why the major part of the phages precipitate in this second step is not fully understood. It seems that this precipitation is partly due to the fact that the solubility of the phages has been slightly decreased due to the previous treatments. This explanation is based upon the fact that the concentration of suspended phages above the precipitate is lower than the concentration of phages in the bottom phase of the first step. No precipitation in the second step occurs if Na dextran sulfate is replaced by dextran.

The yield of phages in this second step is 80–90 per cent. Since the yield of the first step was 60–70 per cent, the final yield of almost pure phages will be 50–60 per cent.

II. Alternate Concentration into the Bottom Phase and the Top Phase

By this method the virus particles are first concentrated, for example, into the bottom phase of a system (see Fig. 7.9); this is collected and mixed with the top phase polymer and suitable salts in such proportions that a small top phase is formed into which the virus particles are concentrated; see Fig. 7.9. This top phase is then collected and mixed with bottom phase polymer and the salt content adjusted, by some means, to that of the first phase system so that a small bottom phase is formed in which the virus particles are concentrated, etc. Theoretically, these procedures can be repeated an infinite number of times.

A system which allows such a concentration is the Na dextran sulfate–polyethylene glycol system at different salt concentrations. As was shown in Table 4.16 of Chapter 4, a number of virus particles distribute in favour of the bottom phase of this system at low NaCl concentrations (0.15–0.3 M), but in favour of the top phase at higher NaCl concentrations (1 M). By adding or removing NaCl and adjusting the polymers to the proper concentrations, the virus particles may thus be pushed either into the top or the bottom phase. This system has been applied to the concentration and purification of ECHO virus and polio virus by a two-step procedure, which will be described below.

(Another system which possibly could be used for the same purpose is the dextran–polyethylene glycol system with different salts. As was demonstrated in Chapter 4 (Figs. 4.15 and 4.20), some proteins distribute in favour of the top phase in the presence of phosphate

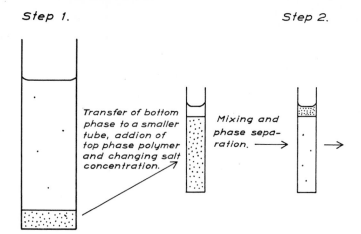

Transfer of bottom
phase to a smaller
tube, addion of
top phase polymer
and changing salt
concentration.

Mixing and
phase sepa-
ration. ⟶

Fig. 7.9. Concentration of particles alternately into the bottom and top phases.

buffer but go into the bottom phase when neutral salts like NaCl,
KCl, or KNO$_3$ are added in excess. Experiments have also been
carried out by applying this system to virus particles (14) for the
purpose of concentrating them alternately into the top and bottom
phases. They were not successful, however, because most of the virus
collected at the interface.)

Applications

5. *ECHO Virus and Polio Virus in the Na Dextran Sulfate–Polyethylene Glycol System*

ECHO virus (12)

Step 1. This is identical with the concentration step described in
section 3 under "One-Step Procedures". It involves a distribution in
a mixture of 0.2 per cent (w/w) NaDS 68 and 6.45 per cent (w/w)
PEG 6000 in 0.3 M NaCl. The small bottom phase into which the
viruses are concentrated, has a composition of 17 per cent (w/w) Na
dextran sulfate and 0.5 per cent polyethylene glycol; see Fig. 2.34.

Step 2. To get a new phase system with the bottom phase from the
previous step, NaCl is added to this phase up to a concentration of
about 1 M; 0.175 ml (=0.2 g) 5 M NaCl is therefore added to each
ml (=1.1 g) of the bottom phase from Step 1. The polymer composi-

TABLE 7.9. *Further concentration and purification (Step 2) of ECHO virus type 7 from a sample of the bottom phase obtained by Step 1; see Table 7.6. This is accomplished by the addition of NaCl to the bottom phase of Step 1 up to a concentration of 1 M. (See text.) From ref. (12).*

Preparation	Volume	Infectivity TCD 50/ml log units	Concentration factor	Nitrogen mg/ml	TCD 50/g protein log units
Bottom phase from Step 1	5	9.3	1	0.790	11.6
Bottom phase (Step 2)	5	8.3		0.640	
Top phase (Step 2)	1	11.8	320	0.86	14.1

tion of this mixture will thus be about 14.4 per cent (w/w) Na dextran sulfate and 0.4 per cent (w/w) polyethylene glycol. It gives a new phase system the top phase of which has a volume of 1/10–1/5 of the total system. Practically all of the virus activity is found in the top phase, as may be seen in Table 7.9 where the results from an experiment are collected.

The yield in activity of the top phase is far higher than one would expect from the amount of virus in the bottom phase from Step 1. This net increase in virus activity has been explained as being partly due to the high salt concentration used in the second step (13). It has thus been reported that an increase in NaCl concentration from 0.15 to 1 M may cause as much as a tenfold increase in virus titre, perhaps due to dissociation of virus aggregates present in the original virus culture (13).

A purification of the virus is also obtained in the second step, since nitrogen distributes almost evenly in the phase system. A particular advantage of the second step is that the virus is transferred into a phase with a low polymer concentration. The concentration of Na dextran sulfate in the top phase is thus only 0.3 per cent (w/w) and polyethylene glycol 1–3 per cent (w/w); see Fig. 2.33. The viscosity of this phase is low and the virus may easily be collected by centrifugation. The remaining dextran sulfate may also be removed by precipitation with KCl or $BaCl_2$.

Polio virus

A similar experiment with polio virus (11) is shown in Table 7.10. As with ECHO virus, most of the virus activity is found in the top phase of the second step.

TABLE 7.10. *Concentration of polio virus by a two-step procedure in the Na dextran sulfate–polyethylene glycol system. Step 1 involves the distribution in a system of 0.2 % (w/w) NaDS 70 and 6.45 per cent (w/w) PEG 6000 in 0.3 M NaCl and Step 2 addition of NaCl to the bottom phase of Step 1 up to a concentration of 1 M NaCl. From ref. (11).*

Preparation	Volume ml	Infectivity TCD 50/ml log units	Concentration factor	Total amount of virus TCD 50
Step 1:				
Original virus culture	200	8.1	1	2.5×10^{10}
Bottom phase	2	10.3	160	$4 \ \times 10^{10}$
Step 2:				
Top phase	0.5	10.8	500	3.2×10^{10}
Bottom phase	1.9	7.7		9.5×10^{7}

III. By "Compression" of One Polymer Phase

The principle of this method is best illustrated by Figs. 7.10 and 7.11, the former showing the phase diagram for two different phase systems. They both have one polymer A in common and we may thus denote them A–B and A–C. Suppose that the virus is distributed in favour of the A-rich bottom phase of both systems. The first and second concentration steps then involve the following procedures.

Step 1. To a volume V_0 of the virus suspension (Fig. 7.11) concentrated solutions of polymer A and polymer B, together having a volume of v', are first added to give a phase system with the composition represented by point P' of Fig. 7.10. A phase, for example the bottom one of this system will have a small volume, V'_b, into which the virus particles are concentrated. The volume of the top phase is V'_t and the partition coefficient is K'. According to eqns. (5) and (6c) the concentrating factor α' of this first step is

$$\alpha' = \frac{V_0}{V'_b \left(1 + \frac{V'_t}{V'_b} \cdot K'\right)} \tag{7}$$

and the yield

$$y' = \frac{100}{1 + \frac{V'_t}{V'_b} \cdot K'}. \tag{8}$$

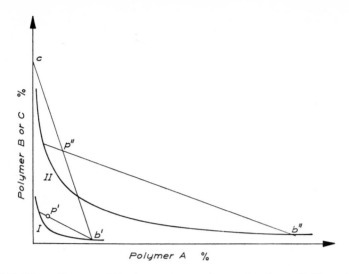

Fig. 7.10. Phase diagrams of the two systems, polymer A–polymer B (I), and polymer A–polymer C (II). For concentration, particles are first distributed in system P' having a small polymer A phase, represented by point b', in which the virus particles are concentrated. Phase b' is collected and a c per cent solution of polymer C (represented by point c) is added so that a polymer composition represented by point P'' is obtained. The virus particles are thereby further concentrated in the small phase b'' of system P''. Compare Fig. 7.11.

Step 2. The composition of the bottom phase of system P' is represented by point b' in Fig. 7.10. A solution of polymer C is added to give a system with the composition P'', which is accomplished by adding a c per cent solution of polymer C to the phase b' in the same weight proportion as the length of the line $\overline{b'P''}$ to the line $\overline{cP''}$. Suppose the volume of the polymer C solution added in this way to the bottom phase b' is v''. In the new phase system P'', the volume of the bottom phase b'' is V_b'' and the partition coefficient is K''. The volume of the top phase is V_t'' and is equal $V_b' + v'' - V_b''$. The concentration factor α'' of the second step is obtained by inserting V_b' for V_0, V_b'' for V_b, V_t'' for V_t, and K'' for K in eqn. (5). Accordingly

$$\alpha'' = \frac{V_b'}{V_b''\left(1 + \dfrac{V_t''}{V_b''} \cdot K''\right)} \tag{9}$$

and in the same way, the yield of the second step will be

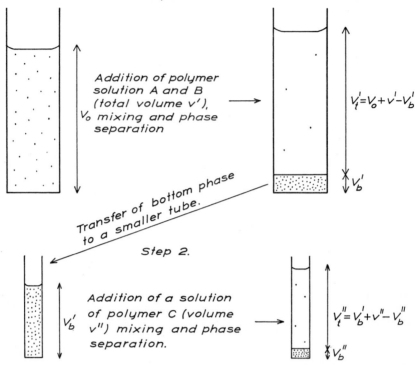

Fig. 7.11. Concentration of particles by compression of one polymer phase. The particles are first concentrated in the bottom phase of a system polymer A–polymer B. A solution of polymer C is added to the bottom phase. After mixing, the bottom phase is then compressed to a smaller volume and the particles further concentrated. Compare Fig. 7.10.

$$y'' = \frac{100}{1 + \dfrac{V_t''}{V_b''} \cdot K''}. \tag{10}$$

The total concentration effect of the two steps will be $\alpha' \cdot \alpha''$, i.e.

$$\alpha' \cdot \alpha'' = \frac{V_0}{V_b'' \left(1 + \dfrac{V_t'}{V_b'} \cdot K\right) \left(1 + \dfrac{V_t''}{V_b''} \cdot K''\right)} \tag{11}$$

and the final yield is $y' \cdot y'' \cdot \frac{1}{100}$ per cent; i.e.

$$y' \cdot y'' = \frac{100}{\left(1 + \dfrac{V_t'}{V_b'} \cdot K'\right) \left(1 + \dfrac{V_t''}{V_b''} \cdot K''\right)}. \tag{12}$$

208

Theoretically, more steps could be made by adding a solution of a third polymer to get a new phase system with a still smaller bottom phase and so on. In practice, however, one is limited by the fact that the concentration of polymer A also increases at each step, resulting in increasingly viscous phases.

By this method the virus particles are concentrated into a phase which is "compressed" to a smaller volume at each step by the addition of a new polymer. Polymers which may be combined to allow such a procedure are, for example, dextran (or Na dextran sulfate), methylcellulose, polyvinylalcohol and polyethylene glycol. Dextran or Na dextran sulfate then plays the part of polymer A in the scheme outlined above and any two of the others become polymers B and C. Examples of applications now follow.

Applications

6. *Adeno Virus and Influenza Virus in the Dextran–Methylcellulose and the Dextran–Polyethylene glycol Systems (14)*

Step 1. This involves the distribution of the virus particles in a system of 0.48 per cent (w/w) D 68 and 0.44 per cent (w/w) MC 4000 which is represented by point P' of the phase diagram of the dextran–methylcellulose system given in Fig. 7.12. (This system is the same as that used for phage T2; see section 2.) 2000 ml of cultures of adeno virus or influenza virus were concentrated and the following mixture prepared:

virus culture	2000 ml
20 per cent (w/w) D 68	52.4 g
MC 4000(+ 80 g 5 M NaCl mixed to a slurry)	9.6 g
H$_2$O	40 g

The dextran solution was first added, then the slurry, the latter being prepared by shaking dry MC 4000 with hot 5 M NaCl and then kept at room temperature. The 40 g H$_2$O were used for washing out the slurry from its flask. After 48 hours for phase separation in the cold (4°C), a bottom phase with a volume of about 140 ml had formed; its virus activity was about 10 times larger than the original culture as may be seen in Table 7.11, where the results of the experiments are given. In this step,

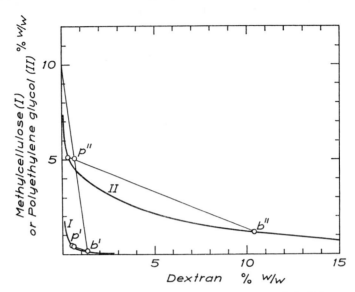

Fig. 7.12. Parts of the phase diagrams of the dextran–methylcellulose system (D 68–MC 4000) and the dextran–polyethylene glycol system (D 68–PEG 6000) used for the concentration of adenovirus and influenza virus by a two-step procedure. The virus is first concentrated into the small phase b' of system P' of the dextran–methylcellulose system. By adding one part of a 10 % solution of polyethylene glycol to one part of the phase b', a dextran–polyethylene glycol system represented by point P'' is obtained. The virus is thereby concentrated into the small phase b'' of this system.

$$V_0 = 2000 \text{ ml}$$

$$v' = 163 \text{ ml}$$

$$V_b'' = 140$$

$$V_t'' = 2023$$

$$K' = 0.01\text{–}0.001$$

By putting these values in eqns. (7) and (8) we should expect

$$\alpha' = 12\text{–}14$$

$$y' = 88\text{–}99 \text{ per cent}$$

Step 2. The bottom phase of the system used in the previous step has a composition of 1.3 per cent (w/w) dextran and 0.15 per cent (w/w) methylcellulose, as judged from the phase diagram; this is represented by b' in Fig. 7.12. In the next step, an equal amount of a 10 per cent (w/w) solution of PEG 6000 is added to this bottom phase and we thus obtain a mixture of 5 per cent (w/w) PEG 6000, 0.65 per cent (w/w) dextran and 0.06 per cent methylcellulose. Neglecting the methylcellulose present, this mixture may be represented by point P'' on the phase diagram of D 68–PEG 6000 in Fig. 7.12. After 24 hours phase separation, the bottom phase represented by point b'' is collected, and has a volume of 10–12 ml; its virus activity is given in Table 7.11. At this step in the experiment with adeno virus,

$$V_b' = 140 \text{ ml}$$
$$v'' = 140 \text{ ml}$$
$$V_b'' = 12 \text{ ml}$$
$$V_t'' = 268 \text{ ml}$$
$$K'' = 0.004\text{–}0.0001$$

We should thus expect, by putting these figures in eqns. (9) and (10), that

$$\alpha'' = 11\text{–}12$$
$$y'' = 93\text{–}100 \text{ per cent.}$$

The total concentration effect of the two steps should be

$$\alpha' \cdot \alpha'' = 130\text{–}170$$

and the final yield

$$y' \cdot y'' = 82\text{–}99 \text{ per cent.}$$

As seen in Table 7.11, the titre of the adeno virus increased from 10^7 to $10^{9.1}$ and that of influenza virus from 8 to 8192. Considering that these figures are very approximate, one can conclude that the concentration effect and yield are in agreement with that expected.

In Table 7.11 the nitrogen content of the different fractions in the experiment with adeno virus is also recorded. It is observed that the concentration of nitrogen does not increase much during the concentration procedures and a purification of the virus in terms of virus activity per mg nitrogen has been obtained. The nitrogen has distributed rather uniformly in both phase systems and it is probable that this represents protein nitrogen since in these systems proteins usually distribute with K values between 0.2 and 5; (see Chapter 4).

TABLE 7.11. *Concentration of adeno virus and influenza virus by a two-step procedure in a dextran–methylcellulose and a dextran–polyethylene glycol system. Data from ref. (14).*

Preparation		Influenza virus		Adeno virus				
		Volume ml	HA-titres	Volume ml	TCD 50/ml log units	Nitrogen mg/ml	TCD 50/mg nitrogen log units	Purification[1] activity/mg N
Original virus culture		2000	8	2000	7.0	0.43	7.4	1
Step 1:								
dextran – methyl-cellulose system	Bottom phase	138	512	140	8.5	0.45	8.8	30
	Top phase	2025	2	2023	6.5	0.39		
Step 2:								
dextran – poly-ethylene glycol system	Bottom phase	10	8192	12	9.1	0.63	9.3	86
	Top phase	266	2	268	6.7	0.20		

[1] Original culture = 1.

The advantage of adding MC4000 as a slurry in 5 M NaCl, lies in reducing the dilution caused by the addition of the polymer solutions. The term v (see eqns. 1–6) then becomes small. It is also more convenient than the rather viscous 2 per cent solution of methylcellulose. However, by the addition of this slurry the NaCl concentration increases from the approximate 0.15 M (physiological saline) of the culture to about 0.3 M. In the second step, where the bottom phase of the first system is diluted with an equal amount of 10 per cent (w/w) PEG6000 (without salt), the NaCl concentration is readjusted to about 0.15 M.

(In principle, the same method could be applied by using Na dextran sulfate instead of dextran. In this case, one may use the system 0.22 per cent (w/w) NaDS68 (or NaDS70) and 0.51 per cent (w/w) MC4000 in 0.15 M NaCl, as in the first step for phage T2 (see above). This gives a small bottom phase with 1.15 per cent (w/w) Na dextran sulfate and 0.2 per cent (w/w) methylcellulose. By adding 1 g of 20 per cent (w/w) PEG6000 in 0.2 M NaCl to each g of this bottom phase, a new smaller bottom phase is obtained. This combination has not, however, been applied so far; it would allow the removal of the dextran sulfate with $BaCl_2$ or KCl.)

7. ECHO Virus in Na Dextran Sulfate–Polyvinylalcohol and Na Dextran Sulfate–Polyethylene glycol Systems (12)

Parts of the phase diagrams of the two systems used in this method, namely the Na dextran sulfate–polyvinyl alcohol and the Na dextran sulfate–polyethylene glycol systems, are given in Fig. 7.13. The results of the experiments are in Table 7.12.

Step 1. This involves the distribution of the virus in a system of 0.3 per cent (w/w) NaDS 68 and 3.0 per cent (w/w) PVA 48/20 in 0.15 *M* NaCl, represented by point *P'* in Fig. 7.13.

5000 ml of culture fluid of ECHO virus type 7 with a titre of $10^{7.1}$ were concentrated and the following mixture prepared:

virus culture	5000 ml
20 per cent (w/w) NaDS 68	102 g
12 per cent (w/w) PVA 48/20	1700 g
NaCl to a final concentration of 0.15 *M*.	

After mixing, and 24 hours phase separation in the cold, a bottom phase with a volume of 237 ml formed. It had a virus activity of $10^{8.5}$, that is, the virus had been concentrated about 25 times. In this step,

$$V_0 = 5000 \text{ ml}$$
$$v' = 1774 \text{ ml}$$
$$V_b' = 237 \text{ ml}$$
$$V_t' = 5537 \text{ ml}$$
$$K' = 10^{-3.6}$$

These values in eqns. (7) and (8) give

$$\alpha' = 21$$
and
$$y' = 99 \text{ per cent.}$$

Step 2. The bottom phase of the system used in the previous step has a composition of 3 per cent (w/w) Na dextran sulfate and 0.5 per

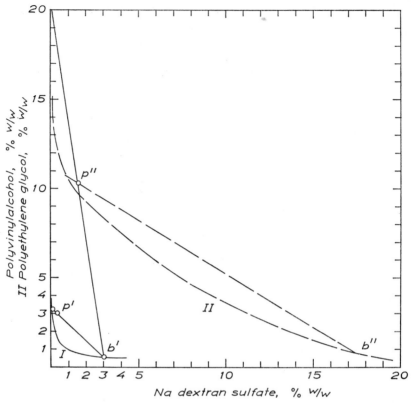

Fig. 7.13. Parts of the phase diagram Na dextran sulfate–polyvinylalcohol (NaDS 68–PVA 48/20 in 0.15 M NaCl) and the Na dextran sulfate–polyethylene glycol system (NaDS 68–PEG 6000 in 0.15 M NaCl) used for concentration of ECHO virus by a two-step procedure. The virus is first concentrated into the small phase b' of system P' of the NaDS 68–PVA 48/20 system. By adding one part of a 20 % (w/w) solution of PEG 6000 in 0.15 M NaCl to one part of the phase b', a dextran sulfate–polyethylene glycol system, represented by point P'', is obtained. The virus is thereby concentrated into the small phase b'' of this system. (The binodial and the tie line of the dextran sulfate–polyethylene glycol system (II) are not known exactly since this phase system has not been analysed in detail, and the salt content of the virus culture was not known exactly.)

cent (w/w) polyvinyl alcohol as found by analysis of the phase; see also Fig. 2.37. This composition is represented by point b' of Fig. 7.13. To each g of this phase, 1 g of a 20 per cent (w/w) solution of PEG 6000 in 0.15 M NaCl is added, to give a mixture of 10 per cent (w/w) PEG 6000, 1.5 per cent (w/w) Na dextran sulfate, and 0.25 per cent polyvinylalcohol. If we neglect the polyvinylalcohol, this mixture may be represented by point P'' of Fig. 7.13.

214

TABLE 7.12. *Concentration of ECHO virus type 7 by a two-step procedure in a Na dextran sulfate–polyvinylalcohol and a Na dextran sulfate–polyethylene glycol system. Data from ref. (12).*

Preparation		Volume ml	Infectivity TCD 50/ml	Concentration factor
Original virus culture		5000	7.1	1
Step 1:				
Na dextran sulfate –	Bottom phase	237	8.5	25
polyvinylalcohol	Top phase	6537	4.9	
system				
Step 2:				
Na dextran sulfate –	Bottom phase	24	9.1	100
polyethylene	Top phase	450	4.5	
glycol system				

After mixing, and 24 hours phase separation in the cold, the bottom phase, represented by point b'', was collected. It had a volume of 24 ml and a titre of $10^{9.1}$. In this step,

$$V'_b = 237 \text{ ml}$$

$$v'' = 237 \text{ ml}$$

$$V''_b = 24 \text{ ml}$$

$$V''_t = 450 \text{ ml}$$

$$K'' = 10^{-4.6}$$

By using these values in eqns. (9) and (10), we obtain $\alpha'' = 10$ and $y'' = 100$ per cent. Theoretically we should expect a total concentration factor of 210 and a final yield of 99 per cent. The uncertainty in the determinations of virus activity does not allow a close comparison with the experimental values, but these are in agreement with what one expects.

In the second step, part of the polyvinyl alcohol was precipitated at the interface of the Na dextran sulfate–polyethylene glycol system. The dextran sulfate of the final bottom phase may be precipitated in the usual way with $BaCl_2$ or KCl. This method has also been applied to the concentration of ECHO virus type 19 (12) in which approximately the same results were obtained.

215

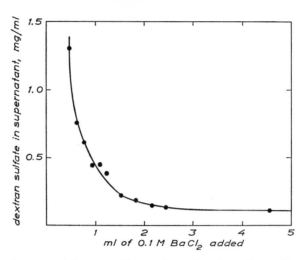

Fig. 7.14. Amounts of dextran sulfate (estimated as the sodium salt) remaining in the supernate after the addition of 1 M BaCl$_2$ to 5-ml aliquots of 2 % (w/w) Na dextran sulfate (NaDS 68). From ref. (12).

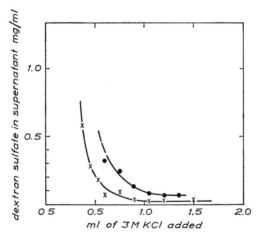

Fig. 7.15. Amounts of dextran sulfate (estimated as the sodium salt) remaining in the supernate after addition of 3 M KCl to 10-ml aliquots of 1 % (w/w) Na dextran sulfate (●), or to 5-ml aliquots of 2 % (w/w) Na dextran sulfate (×). The Na dextran sulfate fraction used was NaDS 68. From ref. (12).

DISCUSSION

The method for concentration and purification of virus presented in this chapter seems to offer many advantages. It is a fairly mild method, which is shown by the fact that no loss in activity from the distribution

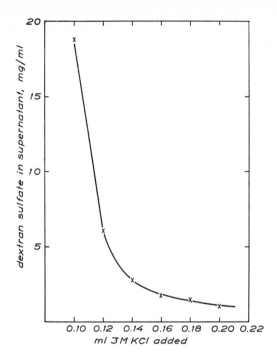

Fig. 7.16. Amounts of dextran sulfate (estimated as the sodium salt) remaining in the supernate after the addition of 3 M KCl to 1-ml aliquots of 17 % (w/w) Na dextran sulfate (NaDS 70). The dextran sulfate was measured polarimetrically.

has been observed. It is believed that this is due to the high water content of the phases and the low interfacial tension between the phases, and the polymers themselves which probably stabilize the virus against denaturation by shaking. It is a well known fact that a virus suspension in an inorganic medium may lose its activity upon shaking. If, however, gelatine or some other colloids are present, this loss in activity is prevented (1). As was mentioned in Chapter 4, methylcellulose or polyethylene glycol stabilize egg albumin against surface denaturation by shaking. An interesting observation in this connection is the stabilizing effect of dextran and Na dextran sulfate on phage T2 against fluorocarbon treatment. If this is a general phenomenon for virus, it would perhaps allow fluorocarbon treatment of a number of viruses which are otherwise too sensitive to this treatment.

An efficient concentration is obtained in a comparatively short time; a concentration of 10 to 100 times may thus be obtained within

10–20 hours in the dextran sulfate–polyethylene glycol system in one operation. This can be carried out in the cold down to about $-5°C$. The systems containing methylcellulose take longer times for phase separation and 24–48 hours are necessary for one operation. By two-step procedures a concentration of as much as 100–10,000 times can be achieved. Since the operations do not require any complicated apparatus, it should be rather easy to apply the method on a large scale for the production of enriched and partly purified virus suspensions. The procedure can easily be carried out under sterile conditions. The distribution is not sensitive to changes in temperature and the polymer concentrations need not be exact, any composition around the given values yielding a suitable phase system. This latter is at least partly due to the polydispersity of the polymers which increases the region in the phase diagram where points represent systems with one small phase; see the shaded areas in Figs. 2.55 and 2.56.

A particular advantage is that the virus particles are not packed into a pellet as during high-speed centrifugation. It is a common experience that such packing may cause losses in virus activity due to aggregation or lysis.

An important result of the experiments reported in this chapter is that a considerable purification in terms of activity per mg nitrogen is obtained, together with the concentration. The purification is caused by: (1) the different distributions of virus and impurities, (2) coprecipitation of impurities with the dextran sulfate precipitate, and (3) the fluorocarbon treatment when this is used.

(1) As a rough guide, proteins distribute rather evenly ($K = 0.5–1$) in the dextran or Na dextran sulfate–methylcellulose systems. In the dextran or Na dextran sulfate–polyethylene glycol systems the K values range between 0.1 and 10. Particles larger than, or of about the same size as the virus particles usually distribute unilaterally or are adsorbed at the interface.

(2) Large cell fragments and whole cells usually coprecipitate with the dextran sulfate precipitate; thus, when the virus activity is concentrated into a dextran sulfate phase together with other cell particles, a major part of these is eliminated by the precipitation. This is shown by the fact that, while the phase containing cell fragments together with the virus is usually very turbid, the supernate after dextran sulfate precipitation is clear and contains most of the virus activity.

(*3*) The effect of the fluorocarbon treatment is not fully understood, but it probably acts as a selective denaturing agent, destroying and collecting various cell fragments and proteins into the fluorocarbon phase (5, 8, 10).

The differential distribution of virus and impurities in the polymer phases, the precipitation of impurities with dextran sulfate, and the fluorocarbon treatment thus probably effect a purification by different mechanisms and used in combination an efficient purification may be achieved. This is exemplified by the isolation of almost pure phage T2 by the Na dextran sulfate–methylcellulose system (7) and ECHO virus by the Na dextran sulfate–polyethylene glycol system (12, 4, 9).

It is generally suggested that concentration and purification in two-phase systems may be used in combination with other methods; thus, after the virus has first been concentrated by two-phase systems from a large volume into a small volume, it may be further treated by other, more refined, methods such as density gradient centrifugation, chromatography and zone electrophoresis.

An often necessary requirement of the method is that the virus particles can be freed from the polymers. This may be accomplished either by washing away the polymers by repeated ultracentrifugations, if they are not damaged by this treatment, or by precipitation of the polymers. Sometimes it may be an advantage to first precipitate the major part of the polymer, such as dextran sulfate with KCl or $BaCl_2$, or methylcellulose with $(NH_4)_2SO_4$, to reduce the viscosity of the virus suspension and then collect the virus particles by centrifugation. In this connection it is important to discuss the amount of a polymer which remains after the major part has been precipitated. Consider, for example, Fig. 7.14. It shows that after the addition of 3 ml 1 M $BaCl_2$ to 5 ml of a 2 per cent (w/w) solution of Na dextran sulfate, about 0.1 mg per ml remains in the supernate, i.e. 99.5 per cent of the dextran sulfate has been precipitated. However, the *number* of dextran sulfate molecules present in the supernate is still considerable compared with the *number* of virus particles. Assuming a molecular weight of 10^6 for Na dextran sulfate there will be, in the above example, about 6×10^{13} dextran sulfate molecules per ml compared with 10^9–10^{12} virus particles per ml. This contamination, although fairly small in weight per cent, may in some cases interfere with the virus. To remove the polymers completely, repeated centrifugations are suggested.

There is also the possibility that the polymers become attached so firmly to the virus particles that they cannot be separated even by careful washing and centrifugations. This possibility has not so far been studied. In general, such a complex formation would be expected to occur more frequently when the polymer is a polyelectrolyte, than when it is a non-ionic polymer.

REFERENCES

1. ADAMS, M. H., *J. Gen. Physiol.*, *31*, 417 (1948).
2. ALBERTSSON, P. Å., *Nature, 182*, 709, (1958).
3. ALBERTSSON, P. Å., and FRICK, G., *Biochim. et Biophys. Acta, 37*, 230 (1960).
4. BENGTSSON, S., HANZON, V., Philipson, L., and WESTMAN, J., *J. Ultrastructure Res.*, in press.
5. EPSTEIN, M. A., *Brit. J. Exptl. Pathol.*, *39*, 436 (1958).
6. FRICK, G., and ALBERTSSON, P. Å., *Nature, 183*, 1070 (1959).
7. FRICK, G., *Exptl. Cell Res.*, (1961) in press.
8. GESSLER, A. E., BENDER, C. E., and PARKINSON, M. C., *Trans. N.Y. Acad. Sci.*, *18(2)*, 701 (1956).
9. HANZON, V., and PHILIPSON, L., *J. Ultrastructure Res.*, *3*, 420 (1960).
10. HOLT, S. J., and EPSTEIN, M. A., *Brit. J. Exptl. Pathol.*, *39*, 472 (1958).
11. NORRBY, E., and ALBERTSSON, P. Å., *Nature*, in press.
12. PHILIPSON, L., ALBERTSSON, P. Å., and FRICK, G., *Virology, 11*, 553 (1960).
13. PHILIPSON, L., personal communication.
14. WESSLÉN, T., ALBERTSSON, P. Å., and PHILIPSON, L., *Arch. Virusforsch.*, *9*, 510 (1959).

8. Antigen–Antibody in Two-Phase Systems

In an immunological reaction the antigen and antibody combine to form complexes which, under optimum conditions, may precipitate or agglutinate. In many cases, such as when the antigen is in excess of the antibody, or when both antigen and antibody are diluted, no precipitation occurs. It is usually then thought that these complexes formed between the antigen and antibody are soluble.

Since these complexes differ in size and possibly in surface properties from the reactants, it is of interest to study the behaviour of an antigen–antibody mixture in a polymer two-phase system. In this chapter, some experiments are described in which mixtures of the proteins phycoerythrin or serum albumin and their respective rabbit antisera are partitioned in the dextran–methylcellulose and dextran–polyethylene glycol systems. In these experiments the distribution of the antigen was studied as a function of the amount of antibody added to a given amount of antigen.

EXPERIMENTS WITH THE DEXTRAN–METHYL CELLULOSE SYSTEM

The following solutions were prepared for a typical experiment.

Antigen. Phycoerythrin in 0.01 M sodium phosphate, pH $=7$, and 0.15 M sodium chloride. Extinction at 540 mμ, 1 cm cell, $=5.0$.

Antibody. Rabbit anti–phycoerythrin serum at different dilutions in 0.01 M sodium phosphate, pH $=7$, and 0.15 M sodium chloride.

Stock mixture of polymers.

2% (w/w) MC 4000	28 g
20% (w/w) D 68	3.2 g
0.05 M NaH$_2$PO$_4$	6.7 g
0.05 M Na$_2$HPO$_4$	6.7 g
1.5 M NaCl	6.7 g
H$_2$O	15.4 g

The contents of the flask are thoroughly mixed prior to removing samples from the stock mixture.

Procedure. 0.2 ml of the antigen solution and 0.8 ml of the antibody solution, containing varying amounts of antiserum, were added to each of a series of tubes of 4–5 ml capacity. Blanks were run on antigen and antibody alone and antigen + normal serum. The contents were mixed and allowed to stand for one hour. 2 g of the stock mixture were then added to each tube. The tubes were inverted several times and allowed to stand for phase separation at 20°C for 15–24 hours. The phase system obtained had a polymer concentration of 0.64 per cent (w/w) D68 and 0.56 per cent (w/w) MC4000. It is represented by a point on the same tie line as system B in Fig. 2.26. After phase separation, samples from the top phase were withdrawn, diluted with water and the extinction measured at 540 mμ. A parallel experiment was carried out in which the antigen was mixed with increasing amounts of antibody without phase system. The amount of antigen remaining in the supernate after centrifugation (3000 g, 15 minutes) was measured by its extinction at 540 mμ.

Results and Discussion

It could be observed that, as more antiserum was added, more antigen colour was transferred to the bottom phase. This was also observed in the antigen excess region where no precipitation occurs. As expected, in the equivalent zone a precipitate was found in the lower part of the bottom phase. The quantitative data are plotted in Fig. 8.1 and show that the decrease in the antigen concentration of the top phase is almost proportional to the amount of antiserum added to the point when nearly all the antigen has been removed from the top phase. Thus, the curve obtained with the phase system is quite different from that of the percentage antigen precipitated by antiserum without the phase system. The latter curve shows the normal shape of a precipitation curve; in the antigen excess region all the antigen remains in solution.

Phycoerythrin, like other proteins, is almost equally partitioned between the phases of the system used here (see Table 4.1). Its partition coefficient is not altered if normal serum is present in the phase system. Gamma globulin, and probably the antibody molecules too, also

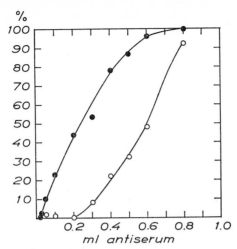

Fig. 8.1. Percentage decrease in antigen concentration in the top phase of the dextran–methylcellulose system (●), and in the supernate of a mixture without phase system (○), as a function of the amount of antiserum added to a given amount of antigen. Antigen: phycoerythrin. To the left is the antigen excess region and to the right the equivalent zone. Room temperature. From ref. (1).

partition roughly equally between the phases. Dextran or methyl-cellulose do not themselves have a significant effect on the precipitation of the antigen when they are present in the same concentrations as in the phase system. Therefore, it seems reasonable to explain the transfer of part of the antigen from the top to the bottom phase in the antigen excess region, as being due to a unilateral distribution of soluble antigen–antibody complexes. As was shown in Chapter 4 (Tables 4.7 and 4.8; Fig. 4.4), the distribution of proteins and viruses depends mainly upon the size, or rather the surface area, of the partitioned molecules and particles. Complexes of a few antigen and antibody molecules would therefore be almost completely collected in the bottom phase of this system. It is also possible, however, that the polymers promote the formation of antigen–antibody complexes.

EXPERIMENTS WITH THE DEXTRAN–POLYETHYLENE GLYCOL SYSTEM

The following solutions were prepared for a typical experiment.

Antigen. Phycoerythrin in 0.1 M potassium phosphate, pH = 7. Extinction at 540 mμ, 1 cm cell, = 2.16.

Antibody. Rabbit anti-phycoerythrin serum at different dilutions dialyzed against 0.1 M potassium phosphate, pH = 7.

Stock mixture of polymers.

50% (w/w) PEG 6000	8.8 g
20% (w/w) D 48	35 g
1 M phosphate buffer, equimolar parts of KH_2PO_4 and K_2HPO_4	5 g
H_2O	1.2 g

Procedure. 0.5 ml of the antigen solution and 1 ml of the antibody solution containing increasing amounts of dialyzed antiserum, were added to each of a series of tubes of 4–5 ml capacity. The contents were mixed and allowed to stand for 1 hour. 1.5 g of the stock mixture were then added to each tube. A system with 7 per cent (w/w) D 48 and 4.4 per cent (w/w) PEG 6000 in 0.1 M sodium phosphate, pH = 7, was thus obtained. After mixing and phase separation for $\frac{1}{2}$–1 hour at 20°C, samples were withdrawn from the top phase, diluted with water and the extinction at 540 mμ measured. Blanks were run on antigen and antibody alone, and antigen + normal serum in the phase system. A parallel precipitation test was run as described above.

Results and Discussion

Phycoerythrin alone, or in the presence of normal serum, partitions in favour of the top phase in this system with 0.1 M sodium phosphate pH = 7 ($K \sim 9$, see Fig. 4.19). Gamma globulin, and probably therefore the antibody molecules, favour the bottom phase ($K \sim 0.5$). Part of the gamma globulin also collects at the interface.

In the tubes in which the antigen and the antibody were mixed, a red precipitate collected at the interface. This increased in volume as more antibody was added. The precipitate was also observed in the antigen excess region. In Fig. 8.2 the percentage decrease in antigen concentration of the top phase is plotted against added antiserum. As with the dextran–methylcellulose system, there is a roughly linear relation between the amount of antigen removed from the top phase and the amount of antiserum added up to concentrations where all the antigen is precipitated at the interface.

However, when the effect on the precipitation reaction of either dextran or polyethylene glycol solutions was studied at the same

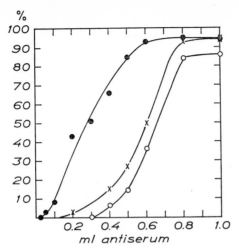

Fig. 8.2. The same as Fig. 8.1 in the dextran–polyethylene glycol system. ×, the same as ○, but at 37°C. From ref. (1).

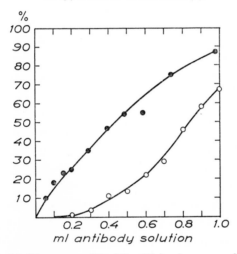

Fig. 8.3. The same as Fig. 8.2, with bovine serum albumin.

found that the polymers also caused precipitation in the tubes with excess antigen.

It is therefore probable that the collection of the antigen at the inter-face of the dextran–polyethylene glycol system is almost entirely due to a decreased solubility of the antigen–antibody complexes in the phases. The fact that one part of the complex, the antigen, has more affinity for the top phase, and another part, the antibody, has more polymer concentrations as occurring in their respective phases, it was

225

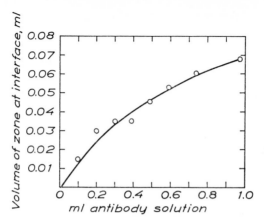

Fig. 8.4. Volume of coloured zone at the interface of a dextran–polyethylene glycol system as a function of amount of antibody added to a constant amount of antigen (coloured bovine serum albumin). The phase separation was allowed to take place in 1 ml pipettes. Ordinate: volume of coloured zone in ml per ml phase system.

affinity for the bottom phase, may also contribute to increasing the collection of the antigen–antibody complex at the interface.

An analogous experiment, with bovine serum albumin coloured by fluorescein isothiocyanate[1] and rabbit anti bovine serum albumin, is shown in Fig. 8.3; it was performed in a similar manner to the previous experiment except that the gamma globulin fraction obtained by precipitation with 40 per cent saturated ammonium sulfate was used. The coloured serum albumin in the top phase was measured by its extinction at 495 mμ. Although serum albumin alone partitions slightly in favour of the bottom phase ($K \sim 0.5$), the result of this experiment is very similar to the preceding one with phycoerythrin.

The coloured precipitate which collects at the interface forms a zone of which the volume can be measured by allowing the phase separation to take place in a narrow graduated pipette of 1–2 ml capacity. The volumes of the zones, measured in this way after 24 hours in the pipettes, are plotted in Fig. 8.4. This manner of following the precipitation of antigen is extremely simple though less accurate than by measuring the extinction of the top phase.

---

[1] The author is indebted to Dr. A. Saha for providing a sample of coloured bovine serum albumin.

CONCLUDING REMARKS

In all these experiments an increased sensitivity in measuring the antigen–antibody reaction in the antigen excess region has been achieved by both phase systems. Thus, when comparatively little antiserum is added to an antigen solution, no precipitation is obtained by the ordinary technique, while a positive reaction may be detected by comparison of the antigen distribution in the phase systems in normal and antiserum. An increase in sensitivity by using a two-phase system is also obtained when the antigen and antibody solutions are dilute. The dextran–polyethylene glycol system thus offers a possibility of concentrating the antigen–antibody precipitate from a large volume of a dilute antigen–antibody mixture into the interface in a narrow tube. It is particularly convenient when the antigen has a specific property such as colour, enzyme activity or biological activity of which the distribution can be followed in the phase system.

In conclusion, it is suggested that polymer two-phase systems may be used with advantage to measure antigen–antibody reactions particularly those which do not give rise to a precipitate.

REFERENCES

1. ALBERTSSON, P. Å., and PHILIPSON, L., *Nature, 185,* 38 (1960).

Summary

The distribution of various cell particles and biological macromolecules in aqueous polymer two-phase systems is described. The particles studied include whole cells, microsomes, bacteriophages, and viruses and the macromolecules studied include proteins in the molecular weight range 50 000–10 000 000 and nucleic acids.

The purpose of this study has been to develop partition methods for characterization and fractionation of biological particles and macromolecules.

The phase systems are constructed by mixing aqueous solutions of two different polymers. A large number of such phase systems have been analyzed in detail; the phase compositions and phase diagrams are given in Chapter 2. The polymers include both non-ionic polymers and polyelectrolytes.

The distribution of a particle depends on the nature and size of its surface and the nature of the phase system. Theoretically, it can be shown that the larger the particle size the more one-sided the distribution. It can also be shown that adsorption of particles at the interface is favoured the larger the particle size and the larger the interfacial tension between the phases.

The experimental results are in qualitative agreement with those expected from theory. Thus, in polymer-polymer two-phase systems, smaller molecules, like the smaller protein molecules, partition evenly between the phases, while larger molecules or particles such as viruses and highly polymerized nucleic acids collect predominantly in one of the phases or at the interface. A relation between the surface area and the partition coefficient of proteins and viruses in a dextran-methylcellulose system has been found.

The phase systems have been used for fractionation of rat brain microsomes and for countercurrent distribution of proteins. The partition of a protein follows the Nernst partition law, that is its partition coefficient is independent on protein concentration and the presence of other proteins. The value of the partition coefficient may thus be used for the characterization of a protein. Considerable fractionation of protein mixtures may be achieved by countercurrent distribution using a dextran-polyethylene glycol system with a suitable salt content.

The phase systems have also been applied for concentration and purification of viruses. By adding polymers in certain proportions to a virus culture, the virus activity may be almost completely transferred to a small volume phase. This procedure can be carried out in several steps. Thus, a virus activity may be concentrated as much as 100–10 000 times. Other substances than viruses, such as proteins and cell fragments, distribute in a different manner in the phase system; a purification of virus is therefore also obtained.

The viruses tested include bacteriophages and a large number of animal viruses. Methods for the preparation of almost pure phage T2 and Echo virus are described.

The distribution of antigen-antibody mixtures in two-phase systems is described. The results show that an increased sensitivity in measuring an immunological reaction in the antigen excess can be achieved by two-phase systems.

Subject Index

DATE DUE

GAYLORD   PRINTED IN U.S A.